thinking out loud

thinking out loud

designing for a positive future

MADE IN BRUNEL™

Made in Brunel
Brunel University, Uxbridge, UB8 3PH
+44 (0) 1895 267 776
www.madeinbrunel.com

Editors: Ian Goodhead
          Sophie Hibbert
          Tim Holley
          Paul Turnock

Type set in Frutiger and Fedra Serif

First published in 2009 in collaboration
with Papadakis Publisher.

PAPADAKIS

An imprint of New Architecture Group Ltd
Head Office: Kimber Studio, Winterbourne
Newbury, Berkshire RG20 8AN
www.papadakis.net

ISBN: 978-1-906506-05-6

natur**ally**responsible

Printed by **Seacourt** to the most stringent environmental systems using **Waterless**
Offset (0% water and 0% Isopropyl alcohol or harmful substitutes), 100%
renewable energy and vegetable oil based inks on paper with at least 50% recycled
content. **Seacourt** is registered to EMAS and ISO 14001, prints to ISO12647 Colour
Standard, is a CarbonNeutral® company and FSC certified TT-COC-2132.

Foreword

Welcome to Made in Brunel
Thinking Out Loud.

The book you are holding is the culmination
of a year-long process that has involved
a dedicated team of students, numerous
academics and a handful of external
supporters. It features the best of Brunel
University's School of Engineering and
Design as well as a selection of innovative
thinking by students from Canada,
China, India and the United States.

The projects featured in this book are
concepts that have been developed over
the past 12 months by a committed group
of students. Their representation on the
following pages denotes a major milestone
in their development and many are now
moving from the academic world into the
commercial realm. The projects highlight
not only the quality of the work produced
by these inspired thinkers but also their
potential to influence the future.

A key aim of Made in Brunel in 2009 has
been to focus on objects, websites and
services that look towards a positive
future. In the current climate of doom
and gloom we hope that we have created
a book that does just that: focuses on
positive thinking that looks to the future
rather than dwelling on the past.

Enjoy looking at the projects
featured in this book and let
them inspire your thinking...

Tim Holley and Nital Patel
Made in Brunel Directors 2009

Supported by

Sponsored by

Autodesk®   Canon   Osborne Clarke   Brunel UNIVERSITY WEST LONDON

Contents

Made in Brunel

Made in Brunel showcases creative talent and is a platform for graduating students to exhibit their ideas.

Now in its fourth year, Made in Brunel in 2009 is building on the success of previous years. Not only are we returning to the Business Design Centre in central London to exhibit our work at the Made in Brunel show, we also have the opportunity to reach out to a much wider audience by displaying our work at events such as the DMY, Berlin, New Designers, London and throughout the London Design Festival.

The Made in Brunel family is growing from year to year. In addition to students from Brunel University's School of Engineering and Design, this year we are joined by students from renowned international universities: Tsinghua University, China; the Indian Institute of Technology, Madras; Rhode Island School of Design, USA; and Simon Fraser University, Canada.

For many years we have enjoyed the support of HSBC Global Education Trust. It is with their support that we have been able to develop our international presence and the Made in Brunel brand. This year we also welcome Autodesk as a major sponsor. Their multinational status and influence in the world of engineering, multimedia and design reflect core values of Made in Brunel. We are also grateful for the support of our other sponsors, such as Osborne Clarke and Canon, whose help has been invaluable in bringing this year's project to fruition.

Made in Brunel has grown since its launch in Brunel's bicentennial anniversary year of 2006. It includes a wide range of projects and disciplines, incorporating the entire School of Engineering and Design. The show has become the destination for consumers, producers and service providers who understand that a synthesis of good design and engineering is a vital function of our lives. It attracts people from across the industry spectrum, whether product or service focused, wanting to meet the young innovators creating our future.

In 2006 the Made in Brunel team set out with the goal of establishing the awareness of the brand and involving a wide range of investors, industries and institutions. In 2009 we are well on the way to further strengthening our brand: international institutions, high profile investors and a broad network of industries are now integral elements of Made in Brunel.

Whilst so much has been achieved over the last four years we are confident that the future is even brighter for Made in Brunel.

MADE IN BRUNEL™

Thinking Out Loud

The theme of Made in Brunel in 2009 is Thinking Out Loud.

In its essence Thinking Out Loud is about people, fun and innovation. It showcases our fresh, forward thinking approach to generating solutions to real life problems.

At its core Thinking Out Loud is focused on the individuality and thought process contained within each project. Although each project may focus on a specific area of thinking, collectively Thinking Out Loud represents a wide range of ideas, thoughts and viewpoints. The common denominator across all of these ideas is that our thinking becomes tangible, we realise our thoughts and we communicate new concepts through a wide variety of media and technologies.

Thinking Out Loud also highlights our role in the future of design, engineering and multimedia. By sharing our thoughts on contemporary issues we firmly place ourselves at the forefront of the next generation of design practitioners.

A number of renowned and respected industry leaders have contributed to this project by thinking out loud about their own area of expertise. This continues the Made in Brunel tradition of connecting theory directly with practice.

Projects featured in this book have been arranged according to the predominant type of thinking featured within them. These types of thinking are:

▦ technical thinking

◌ sustainable thinking

◩ 4dimensional thinking

ⅱ humanistic thinking

The range of projects featured in each section underlines the depth and scope of each area. Many of the projects are multifaceted and their areas of depth are represented by the icons featured on each page.

thinking out loud

"Isambard Kingdom Brunel was a genius of his generation – pioneering, creative, daring and forward thinking. He took these ideas and used them to do amazing things – making steel float and building marvels of engineering. Just as these qualities opened up new horizons in his lifetime, so Made in Brunel inspires and creates the designers of tomorrow"

Jeremy Clarkson

Isambard Kingdom Brunel
(1806-1859)

In the 100 years up to 1860 the work of a small group of engineers made possible the economic and social upheaval in Britain that we call the Industrial Revolution. Brunel, perhaps, was the most prodigious of them. Many of his works, which challenged and inspired his colleagues during this period, have survived to our own time, and some are still in use today.

He was born in Portsmouth in 1806, the son of a distinguished French engineer, Sir Marc Brunel, who had come to England at the time of the French Revolution. Unlike most engineers of the time, Isambard Kingdom Brunel received a sound education and practical training before entering his father's office at the age of 20 and taking full charge of the Thames Tunnel project from Rotherhithe to Wapping.

At the age of 26 he was appointed Engineer to the newly-formed Great Western Railway and acted with characteristic boldness and energy. His great civil engineering works on the line between London and Bristol, are still used by today's high-speed trains and bear witness to his genius. His designs encompassed not just the rails, but also viaducts and stations, including Bristol Temple Meads, at the time the biggest railway station in the UK. He eventually engineered over 1,200 miles of railway, including lines in Ireland, Italy and Bengal.

In 1831 his designs won the competition for a bridge across the River Avon which he began, but did not have time to complete in his lifetime. The Clifton Suspension Bridge, as it became known, was finished in 1864 in Brunel's honour by his engineering friends and is still in use today.

Isambard Kingdom also designed ships. Each of his three projects represented a major step forward in naval architecture. The 'Great Western', launched in 1837, was the first steamship to engage in transatlantic service. The 'Great Britain', launched in 1843, was the world's first iron-hulled, screw propeller-driven, steam-powered passenger liner. The 'Great Eastern', launched in 1859, was designed in cooperation with John Scott Russell, and was by far the biggest ship ever built up to that time, but was not commercially successful.

Brunel's other works included docks, viaducts, tunnels, buildings and the remarkable prefabricated hospital, with its air-conditioning and drainage systems for use in the Crimean War. Inevitably, in such a prolific career, there were setbacks and disappointments such as the atmospheric railway, but he readily admitted his mistakes. Indeed he himself suffered financially by supporting his ventures with his own money.

As his sketch-books and note-books show, he concerned himself with every aspect of the projects in which he was involved from the grace of the design to the precision of the execution. His great achievement was to marry his vision of how things could be done better with the calculation and experiments required to make it possible. Brunel died of a stroke on 15th September 1859.

Despite the short duration of his illustrous career, he was one of the greatest entrepreneurs who made the Industrial Revolution possible. His great achievements remain to this day an inspiration to designers and engineers the World over and his example is a particular inspiration to the staff and students of the university which is named after his honour.

The School of Engineering and Design

We form the dynamic core of Brunel University, a powerhouse of innovative thinking and applied ideas. At the heart of the School of Engineering and Design is a community of incredibly motivated young people who form one of the largest and most successful Design and Engineering Schools in the UK. We are recognised, worldwide, as a centre of excellence and have established Brunel as the incubation arena for applied thinking, innovative problem solving and commercially attractive ideas.

The School is home to over 2500 undergraduate, postgraduate and research thinkers – a veritable factory of ideas. The projects within this book and in our London exhibition bring together the best of this broad-based team, and bring together like-minded innovative thinkers from across the world. We are an optimistic and proactive team, working alongside industrial partners in the manufacturing and service sectors, gaining industrial experience on the way, and moving into the broadest range of companies and organisations to provide a world of future thinking.

We are the shapers of the future and have this extraordinary book to showcase those ideas.

Brunel University

Brunel is a world-class university based in Uxbridge, West London. Born just over 40 years ago, Brunel's distinctive mission has always been to combine academic rigour with the practical, entrepreneurial and imaginative approach pioneered by our namesake Isambard Kingdom Brunel.

As befits a university with Brunel's history and reputation, research is at the heart of all we do. It underpins and contributes to the generation of most of our taught courses. Moreover, Brunel's research ethos generates a culture of intellectual endeavour that is fundamental to the achievement and success of all students and staff of the University. It also encourages the cross-fertilisation of ideas and expertise for which we have long been famous.

Brunel University's influence extends far beyond the fields of engineering, science and technology, which were its original strengths. A long succession of developments and mergers, particularly those which transformed Acton Technical College into Brunel University and later saw Brunel Merge with Shoreditch College and West London Institute, has brought the University from modest beginnings to a major force on the UK higher education sector.

Building a New Brunel

The University is nearing completion of its £250 million campus redevelopment programme and now possesses an impressive range of facilities, including:

- UEFA-class football facilities, competition-standard athletics complex and refurbished sports and fitness centre;
- Extended library building, holding a hugely increased book and journal collection, computer workstations and group study areas, an Assistive Technology Centre for disabled students z and a café;
- 34 halls of residence, including a new residential complex that brings our on-campus accommodation up to 4,549 rooms;
- Health Sciences and Social Care building, opened by Her Majesty The Queen;
- New Engineering and Design annex and atrium, including an impressive exhibition space;
- Student facilities complex with a stunning atrium entrance opening onto a dining space, bars, the Students' Union and retail outlets.

The student community includes an international contingent some 1,600 strong, drawn from 110 countries. Just as Isambard Kingdom Brunel opened up new horizons for the Victorians through his engineering innovations, so Brunel University has helped successive generations to expand their horizons by creating opportunities for students to acquire new knowledge. Since the 1960s the name of Brunel University has been synonymous with the provision of high quality academic programmes, which meet the needs of the real world and contribute in a very practical way to progress in all walks of life.

We are exceedingly proud of our university, and of it's many contributions to the empowerment of individuals and to the progress of society.

technical

Products and concepts which are innovative in their use of manufacturing, material and electronic technologies.

Technologies are continually developing, creating new and innovative possibilities. Technical thinking embodies reapplying existing technologies to new situations to create innovative design solutions. It is this type of thinking that pushes boundaries and questions what can be done, resulting in great advances and shaping the future.

thinking

Future Concepts for Canon

Through focused creative thinking and brand analysis, Canon's core values were distilled to 'enriching vision'. This encompasses everything from improving the way in which we do and see things to preserving and improving the world for future generations.

This design philosophy has been followed to inspire and direct four new product themes on a functional and visual level.

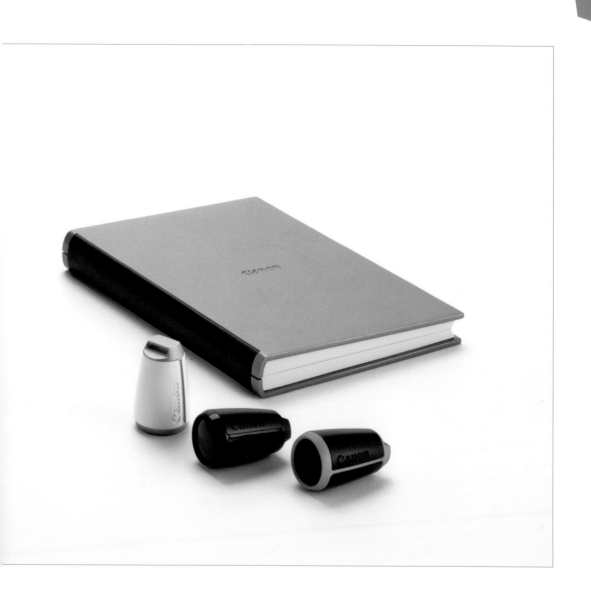

Joe Allum
Industrial Design & Technology BA

Canon Wild
Future concept for Canon

The Canon conservation device is a small device linked via satellite to a specific endangered species. The device will throb to the exact heart beat of the living animal allowing readings to be monitored, which can be used to decipher what the animal's doing at that exact moment in time. Readings and movements of the animal will be online for the holder of the Canon Wild to check up on as well as for the conservationists to keep and eye on the animals well being. The idea of the Canon Wild is to create a link between the animal and the holder of the device and to raise awareness of endangered species.

Rob Fuller
Industrial Design BSc

Canon Vision
Future concept for Canon

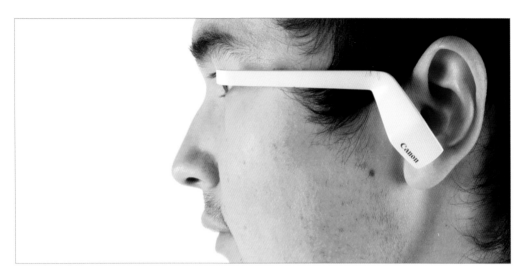

Canon products provide the gateway for images between the online and offline worlds. By using virtual retina display technology the Canon Vision is able to pass digital images almost directly to the optic nerve without the need for invasive implants.

By augmenting additional digital information with the user's sight, they are able to seamlessly view enriched information about the task in hand allowing increased technical ability and efficiency.

Tim Holtom
Industrial Design & Technology BA

Canon Album
Future concept for Canon

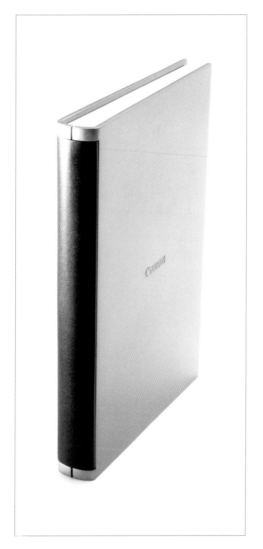

The future will hold many information rich digital images. The Canon Album is a place where all these images are stored. Meta data allows for intiuitive navigation through use of its ergonomically designed, topographic touch screen.

Images can also be easily mounted to any surface, including glass, using artificial 'gecko foot' grip characteristics situated on its hinge.

James Vardy
Industrial Design BSc

Canon Soap
Future concept for Canon

590 million people are at risk globally from the largest form of infectious blindness, Trachoma. Trachoma is an infection which spreads as a result of poor personal hygiene. 90% of the affected areas are dry, rural, sections of the developing world. With basic cleaning products such as soap, the spread of this horrific infection could be controlled and brought to a halt.

Canon Soap processes everyday cooking by-products to generate soap in a safe way and in doing so gives the user and their community the chance to see.

Future Concepts for Clinique

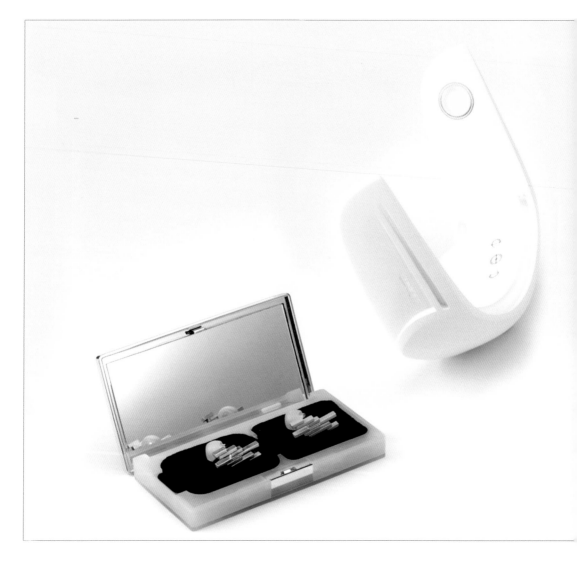

Clinique is a scientifically based cosmetic brand, whose carefully tailored products help empower individuals to feel beautiful.

Clinique's main product focus is a three-step skin-care system that encourages beauty through confidence. Beauty is more than skin deep and these future concepts have been developed as guidance system towards a healthier lifestyle.

In a future world where individuals have little time, these concepts look to restore balance to their everyday life, improving their personal well-being and confidence levels.

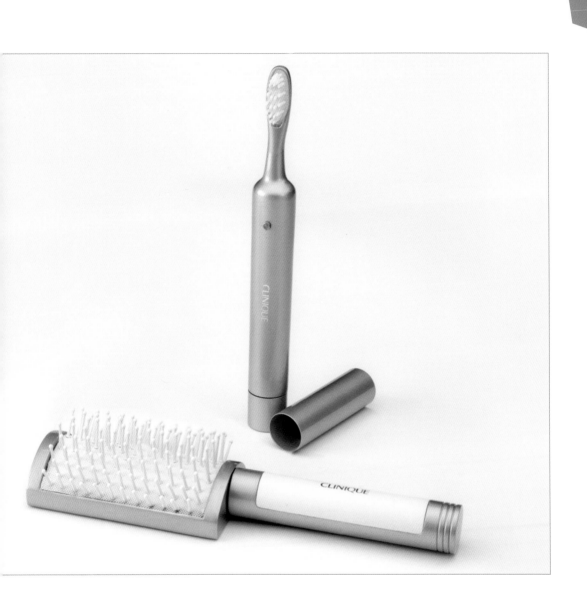

Sophie Hibbert

Industrial Design BSc

Clinique Perfect Equilibrium Lifestyle Monitor

Future concept for Clinique

Clinique's latest accessory adorns your ear discreetly, monitoring your individual health. Not only does it enhance your looks with its beautiful form, but it also provides you with the necessary information to enable you to balance your lifestyle. By monitoring your heartbeat, voice levels and temperature it will provide you confidentially with guidance as to how to make the subtle changes which will keep you healthy and beautiful. Wireless connectivity enables you to use the Perfect Equilibrium Lifestyle Monitor as a universal headset for your PMDs (Personal Media Device), making it an indispensible part of your Clinique lifestyle.

My-Binh Ly
Industrial Design BSc

Clinique Solace Sleep Assistant
Future concept for Clinique

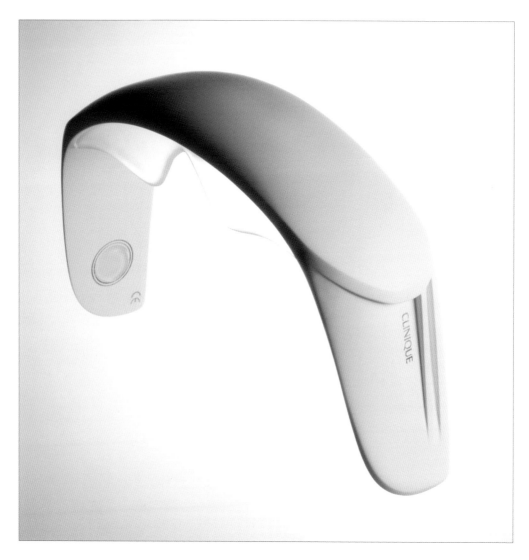

We spend approximately a third of our lives sleeping. It plays a vital part in helping to re-nourish our body and mind, being essential in maintaining normal cognitive skills. Stress and worry can lead to difficulties sleeping, with sleep deprivation causing reduced performance during the day.

The Solace Sleep Assistant sends gentle pulses to the temporal region of the head to massage the day's build up of stress away, helping the individual to relax and drift off to sleep. The intelligent sleeping mask also monitors the user's R.E.M sleep, so they are able to build up a sleep log throughout the year.

Victoria Monks
Industrial Design BSc

Clinique Interactive Health Hair Brush
Future concept for Clinique

People have busy lifestyles and often do not take the time to look after themselves, sometimes missing the signs that the body is run-down or in poor health. This product combines the function of the hair brush with a self-monitoring system, where the information is fed back to the user through a bespoke Clinique interface.

The product will become part of people's normal daily routine to build a profile of its users through measuring the pulse, grip, hydration and other health indicators.

The product encompasses the brand values of Clinique and takes an enabling approach to help the users help themselves.

Sabrina Tan
San Francisco State University

Clinique Integrated Dental Diagnostic System
Future concept for Clinique

This product uses ultraviolet blue light to clean and brighten teeth while disinfecting and sanitising the bristles. Radiation from the blue light is filtered through the micro-layers of the clear carbon plastic toothbrush head. The bristles are made of special high density fibres to last three times longer than normal bristles.

Sensors are built into the toothbrush head to monitor hydration levels through the user's saliva. This information is sent wirelessly to the mirror interface notifying the user of their hydration level. The docking base charges the toothbrush and detaches to plug into the wall with flip up and down prongs.

Future Concepts for Roberts

In the past decades, Roberts has put its brand identity at risk by attempting to lower its prices and quality to meet today's competitive market. Roberts' history has been retraced and identified and their values of quality, tradition and craftsmanship that established their name will continue in the future.

This new line of products is focused on improving home ambiance by stimulating the senses and changing the mood, thus enhancing the experience the users get from owning a Roberts product.

Ainur Orazbayeva
Industrial Design BSc

Roberts Always-in-Mood
Future concept for Roberts

Mood is an emotional aspect affecting our lives greatly. Imagine being able to choose your mood, for example feeling happier after a stressful day, having the ability to concentrate on work or create a specific atmosphere in your home?

The new product for Roberts, a famous traditional radio manufacturer, aims to improve users' emotional state by choosing a desirable mood from the scents library.

Using a microcontroller, it releases scents in small portions, affecting humans on subconscious levels. These are mixed in specific proportions from basic scents in rechargeable cartridges. The product brings together the heritage of a respected and trusted brand and modern digital technology, presented to the user in a simple and understandable way.

Esteban Schunemann
Industrial Design & Technology BA

Roberts LP25 light capturing device
Future concept for Roberts

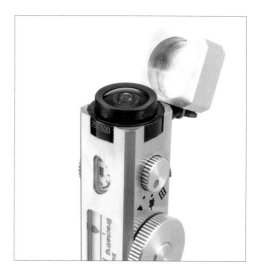

By capturing the light intensity and colour from all directions, the Roberts LP25 memorises life.

It might be a sunrise in Japan, or a sinister alley under a full moon. The LP25 will record the spirit of a place which is more substantial and memorable than just taking a picture. The captured experiences can be relived later at home using the central console linked up to a specialised lighting system. This can recreate, in a home environment, memories and ambience that would otherwise be lost in alternative media.

Juan Francisco Veramendi
San Francisco State University

Roberts Home Projector
Future concept for Roberts

Simple, compact, versatile and most importantly, Roberts. Enjoy your favourite pictures, home videos and movies the way they were meant to be seen; on the big screen. Leave aside your television and place the Home Projector anywhere at anytime. Roberts Home Projector brings the latest technology, ultracompact HD resolution images and high fidelity wi-fi surround sound speakers. So sit back and enjoy your videos and pictures with the excellent quality that has made Roberts the product you and your family have been proud to use for over 70 years.

Engineering the Legacy

Marcus Abbott

I find the recent debate between William McGrath, Chief Executive of Aga and George Monbiot of The Guardian, on the environmental impact of the famous cookers prompts some thought; as designers and engineers, should we focus on short-term 'real-time' energy efficiency and environmental impacts, or should we take a long-term view?

I think, of course, the answer is both. However, I'm increasingly aware that both the media and legislation encourages us to pay more attention to the former, sometimes to the detriment of the latter, leading to possibly ill-conceived design and purchase decisions. For example, currently the only measure of environmental impact that an automobile makes, and widely publicised to inform and influence, are the CO_2 emissions in use. Similarly, fridges, washing machines and dishwashers are required to clearly display EU Energy Consumption Labels in the showroom. Even our houses are required to have an Energy Performance Certificate published by vendors as part of the Home Information Pack. But I think none of these measures do justice to life-time environmental impacts, nor do they ensure product quality, appropriate use of resources, or the longevity that can be encouraged by truly engaging design. I read a recent report that suggests the Toyota Prius is expected to last less than half as long as a Mercedes CLS (and interestingly costs about half the price), yet I find no indicator that clearly, readily and uniformly informs me about environmental life-cycle impacts, and particularly the complete CO_2 emissions of produce, use and disposed, for either product.

Recently, the combination of both environmental and economic concerns has led to a distinct media backlash against expensive luxury products. I think this is almost certainly as much to do with symbolism as anything rational, yet in so doing it may reinforce short-term environmentalism and accelerate the cadence of consume and dispose. Many 'luxury' products, by their nature, are skilfully designed and engineered to engage over long periods of time and are made with materials that last by crafts-people whose artisanship is evident in every detail. Some objects become so emotionally valuable that they are passed through family generations. Some luxury brands offer restoration services to prolong product life. It is possible that many of these products are less environmentally damaging, long-term, than alternatives that are promoted to be 'good', but how do I know and how do I judge them without bias?

In fact, sometimes I think we are explicitly encouraged not to answer the 'complete' environmental question; the government has recently announced a £5000 incentive scheme for us to dispose of old direct fossil-fuelled vehicles and buy an electric vehicle, no matter how the energy to run the car is produced, or how long the new product may last, whilst the London Congestion Charge penalises small diesel cars that emit more than a third less average CO_2 than some hybrids that are exempt. Both of these initiatives seem more about headline grabbing rather than truly informed decision making. I think the risk is they may improperly influence purchase decisions and consequently product development strategies that may leave a more harmful environmental legacy than originally (and naively) intended.

Whilst some limited progress has been made to understand product life-time effects, our knowledge is currently immature and certainly not disseminated to the high street. What I need is to be properly informed by a balanced view, in both legislative and cultural terms, of low-damage environmental choice through standardised, transparent and unambiguous measures of life-cycle environmental impact as well as 'real-time' energy efficiency. More focused research and a more receptive audience is needed here. I also think that if industry, designers and marketers can address the current imbalances by striving to develop products that consider true life-time environmental impacts, we can responsibly engineer great product diversity that leaves a positive and enduring legacy.

Marcus Abbott
Engineering and Branding Researcher

Myles William Bigden
Product Design BSc

Fugu*
A light controlled playfully, through sound and movement

Fugu is a fun imitation of a puffer fish's defence mechanism. In the form of a light, its instinctive animalistic behaviour is replicated by a mechanical and electronic system.

When threatened by high levels of noise or intimidating close presence, Fugu's heartbeat increases, pushing out all of its 31 glowing red spikes. When calm, its heartbeat drops, retracting all of its spikes returning to a relaxed state.

Fugu is a light which allows the user to playfully influence its behaviour through sound and movement resulting in a variety of light levels.

John Andrew Brackett
Product Design BSc

Pitch Presto
Transform the pitch of your drum in a beat

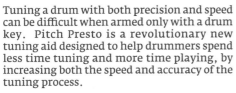

Tuning a drum with both precision and speed can be difficult when armed only with a drum key. Pitch Presto is a revolutionary new tuning aid designed to help drummers spend less time tuning and more time playing, by increasing both the speed and accuracy of the tuning process.

The lightweight aluminium tuning ring fits around the rim of the drum, locking onto each tuning rod and enabling simultaneous adjustments. One quick twist of the drum key achieves quick and even tuning results.

Joel Brasher-Jones
Sports Technology BSc

Talons Stud Design
A stud for the future to prevent ankle injury

Ankle injury is one of the main causes of injury in rugby. These studs were designed to increase the grip on the surface therefore preventing the ankle from rolling. After testing, the results showed that the studs improved players' performances. These studs can be adjusted for the player's needs.

With rugby players getting faster all the time, the smallest of margins are the difference between scoring a try and getting tackled. This is why customisation of the studs will help improve players' performances.

The pictures show the studs set up for ultimate grip going forward and for the best grip for performing a sidestep.

David Brown
Product Design BSc

Clear Vision
Cleaning system for exterior cameras

More and more automotive companies are integrating external camera systems into their vehicles to act as driver aids. Due to the harsh weather conditions that vehicles operate in, vision through these systems can become substantially reduced.

The product developed integrates nano cleaning technology with rear vision cameras, which keeps exterior camera lenses clear from the mud, grime and pollution that is present on today's roads. A fully working prototype was produced to demonstrate how the system would function if incorporated into a vehicle.

Cocktail Sidekick
Fully automated spirit dispenser

Cocktail sidekick magically delivers your
desired drink without you even having to lift
a finger, well almost... Match up the coloured
bottle holders with the coloured buttons,
select your drink of choice and watch while
your drink is served. The machine has a
capacity of four bottles and even comes with a
selection of cocktails already programmed.

Anthony James Case
Industrial Design & Technology BA

Smart Hands
Wireless communications glove for a motorcycle rider

The wireless communication glove has been created with the aim of improving the experience of long distance motorcycle riding. The glove acts as a controller to allow riders to operate certain electronic items which car drivers have become accustomed to using.

The purpose of the glove is to enable riders to control items such as music players and satellite navigation tools, in a safe and reliable manner.

By squeezing the handle bar with each finger, the rider is able to adjust and control different functions, such as changing the volume of a music player or reprogramming a GPS system, without the need to remove their hands from the handle bars. The gloves have been tested by DSA approved riding instructors.

Mabasa Chakawhata

Mechanical Engineering BEng

Heat Transfer Enhancement of Phase Change Materials

Melting and solidification using fluent computational method

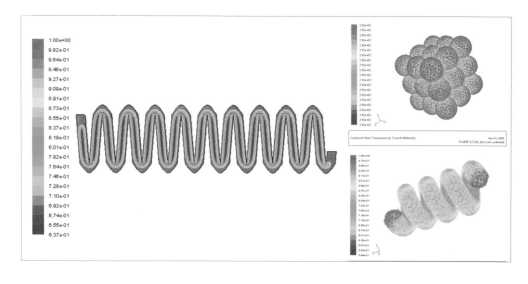

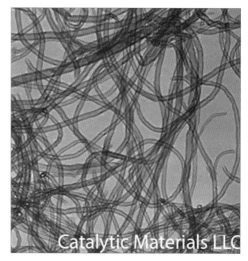

The project concerns the heat transfer enhancement of Phase Change Material (PCMs) by utilising multi-walled carbon nanotubes in a composite with PCMs.

PCMs are materials that have a high latent heat of fusion (the energy needed to change phase from solid to liquid or vice versa). Due to these natural characteristics, a PCM can be applied in a building space to passively or actively absorb heat. As a result, the sensible cooling load on an air-conditioning plant for example, can be reduced. Organic PCMs have poor thermal conductivity, therefore the effects of high thermal conductivity carbon-nanotubes are being investigated using Computational Fluid Dynamics (CFD).

Louise Charouneau
Industrial Design & Technology BA

Red Eye
Smart clothing security ink tag

Shoplifting in the retail industry has increased dramatically in recent years, with current security methods failing to provide a deterrent for today's shoplifter.

The smart ink tag operates by releasing permanent ink over the attached garment if it is removed from the premises . The radio frequency present across the current retail security barriers is used to activate the release of the dye, causing damage to the clothing which subsequently causes the act of shoplifting to become pointless. The accompanying awareness campaign completes the deterrent by alerting potential shoplifters to the security system, forcing them to reconsider.

like red?

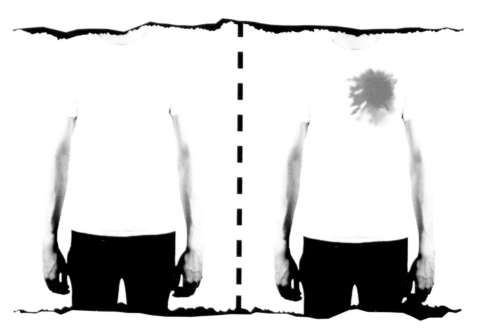

love shoplifting...

shoplifters beware, this store uses 'red eye', attempts to remove garments will cause damage

red eye

Jack Cheatle
Industrial Design & Technology BA

Pedalock
The worlds first detachable bicycle pedal with integrated lock

"In the UK, a bicycle is stolen every minute and less than 5% of those are returned to their owners." Metropolitan Police 2008

The Pedalock is an innovative new design that integrates a detachable bicycle pedal with an in-built lock. The custom machined lock has been designed to fit within the dimensions of a bicycle pedal making it available for the cyclist at all times. The Pedalock is designed to help in the prevention of bicycle theft by removing the opportunity and desire to steal. This is achieved by incorporating the removal of the pedal into the design of the lock.

Hence if the lock were to be breached the thief would be left with a pedal-less bicycle, which greatly reduces its desirability, as it is now far harder to cycle away.

Gavin Chetty
Industrial Design BSc

Orthotic Design
Insole orthoses to treat fallen arches and correct posture

It is vital for a person's biomechanical system to operate efficiently. When this system degenerates, as it often does in the foot, resulting in fallen arches, there is a knock-on effect on body posture and gait. These insole orthoses tie together the latest theories and technology in the podiatric industry.

The new orthoses aim to stabilise posture and improve the mobility of patients. The new design has been extensively tested using the latest gait analysis equipment and 3D foot scanning hardware courtesy of London Orthotic Consultancy.

Dulux Play
Future concept for Dulux

Dulux Play is a desktop entertainment device that monitors the user's emotional reaction to music and creates a customised playlist according to the user's current mood.

If they wish to alter their mood they can change the emotional context of the playlist by using a jog-dial and touch screen interface on the top of the product.

This product promotes the Dulux brand values of self-expression and identity by enabling the user to express their individuality through their choice of music.

Dulux Play promotes tactile and theatrical interaction with digital music devices.

Matthew Cristofoli

Industrial Design & Technology BA

Re-Flow

Pneumatic compression therapy, for the treatment of Chronic Vascular Insufficiency (CVI)

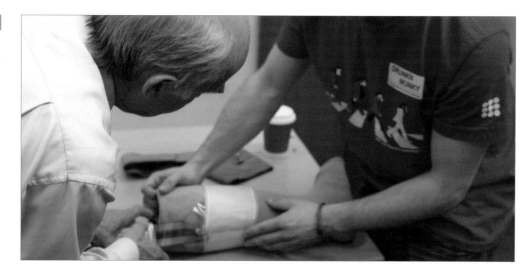

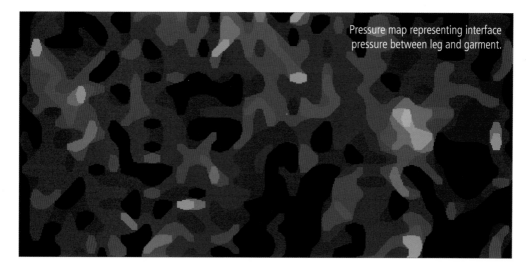

Pressure map representing interface pressure between leg and garment.

Between 2005 and 2006 the NHS spent roughly £100,000,000 on the treatment of Chronic Venous Insufficiency, a medical condition involving reduced blood flow from the leg arteries to the heart. The majority of the patients are aged between 59-75. With a wide range of other health issues, these people are susceptible to contracting further illnesses.

With patients' compliance, current leg compression garments prescribed by health care professionals can improve symptoms within three to four weeks. However, a proportion of this user group experience difficulties stemming from reduced dexterity in applying the prescribed garment.

For this reason the current solutions can be problematic, and this project aims to develop a graduated compression stocking that provides a more user-friendly alternative to those currently available.

> "22% of patients suffering from Cellulitis are aged between 60-74 and 35% were aged 75+."

This condition places a large strain on the NHS and other health services worldwide. The author aims to design a solution to reduce this statistic using a new form of pneumatic compression therapy.

Matt Cristofoli

Ryan Lloyd Dee
Industrial Design & Technology BA

Match Winning Catch
Portable rugby training machine to maximise training sessions

Electrically powered rugby training machine to help improve individual's or group's catching abilities or to perfect play through repetition, thus maximising efficiency of the training session while building upon the user's kinesthetic awareness. The user will be able to trigger the release and fire a rugby ball using wireless technology.

This enables a single person to be able to train for certain real life game scenarios without assistance from a training partner or coach.

The wireless controls also means individuals or coaches who are not involved in the exercise can supervise from an appropriate spot during the drill aiding in extrinsic feedback.

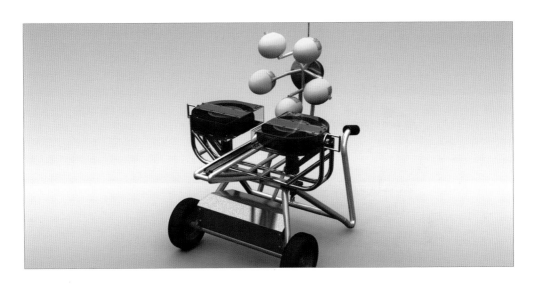

Rob Fuller

Industrial Design BSc

Soft Pump

A 'soft' linear peristaltic pump

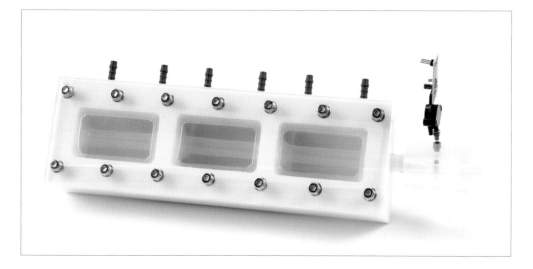

A compressed gas actuated linear peristaltic pump concept which facilitates biologically appropriate flow conditions and gas exchange. Prototypes were designed and developed to demonstrate the concept and quantify mechanical and biological performance, compared to target data.

The Soft Pump has the potential to provide a simple and effective cell culturing system for micro-organisms and primary cells, which could aid the development of stem cell therapies. Supported by Tony Anson.

Ian Goodhead
Product Design BSc

Neuro Pong
Neural interface computer game

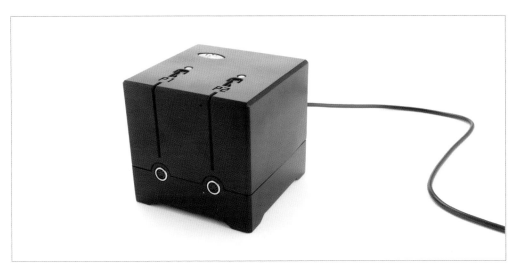

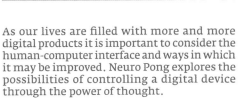

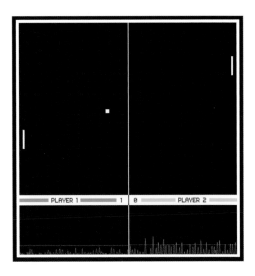

As our lives are filled with more and more digital products it is important to consider the human-computer interface and ways in which it may be improved. Neuro Pong explores the possibilities of controlling a digital device through the power of thought.

The product monitors the user's brain activity through sensors placed on the forehead. Data collected is interpreted and used to control a simple two player recreation of the classic arcade game PONG.

Oli Gould

Industrial Design BSc

ORCA

A portable device to aid hydration in athletes

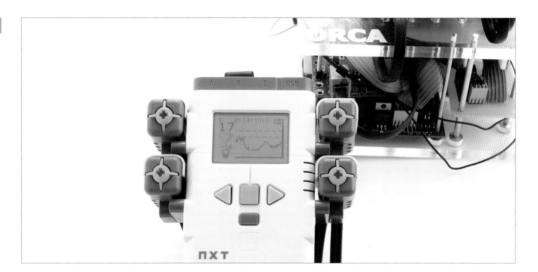

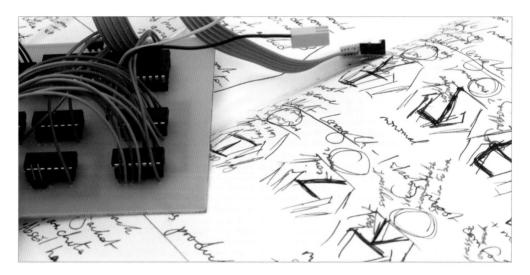

Athletes frequently underestimate fluid loss through sweat and as a result, fail to hydrate adequately. Minimising dehydration is considered the simplest, yet most effective step athletes can take to protect their health and optimise performance:

2% of bodyweight dehydration results in a 20-30% decrement in performance.

ORCA monitors the user's hydration status and communicates the correct fluid intake in real-time. Based on cognition and interaction theory, conversation between user and device has been designed so as to minimise training disruption.

The device also reviews progress over time and returns heart rate information.

Mark Haite
Industrial Design & Technology BA

Joe Spresso
Portable espresso machine

Next to water, coffee is the most consumed beverage in the world. Joe Spresso aims to target people on the move, by giving the consumer the ability to make a smooth, intense espresso when there is no café nearby. The product is a revolutionary design, which allows the user to quickly and easily make a coffee house standard espresso.

The product is aimed at a wide demographic, including individuals who enjoy hiking and camping, to those who have a long commute to work. The device brightens a person's day, and give them the kick-start they need.

Sandy Holford
Product Design Engineering BSc

The Wingman
Remotely activated romantic mood setter

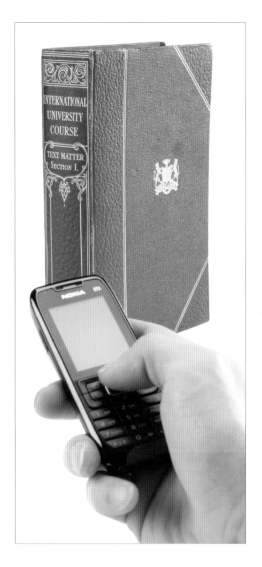

This product enables the owner to contact his house via mobile phone during an evening to alert the house to the likelihood of a guest being brought home. The base unit then prepares the house ready for their return.

Either with a comforting hot chocolate for one, or by enabling mood lighting, music, and chilling a bottle of wine so the house is ready to impress. The device can be used to activate any mains powered appliance.

WeatherGnome

Automated temperature controlled clothing selection

A temperature sensor disguised as a garden gnome wirelessly transmits data into the house. The corresponding unit inside is a wardrobe. This wardrobe displays the temperature outside in real-time. It also rotates the hanging rail so that the user is offered the correct type of clothing for the weather conditions outside. This allows the user to be fully prepared for the current weather conditions without going outside.

Sahir Khan
Mechanical Engineering BEng

Structural Analysis of a Microlight Aircraft
Structural analysis of the MW6T Merlin using computational techniques

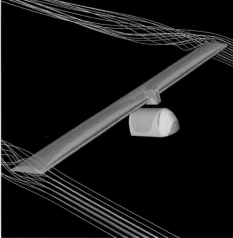

The MW6T Merlin is a single engine, two passenger light aircraft with a high mounted wing and a simple structural layout. The project involved analysing the effects of various operational load cases on the aircraft's structure using computer based simulation. These load cases included in-flight as well as landing loads, which were identified using a combination of computational fluid dynamics as well as classical engineering statics and dynamics. The loads were then applied to a finite element model of the aircraft where the corresponding stress distributions and deflections were observed and interpreted.

Frankie Lathbury
Product Design BSc

EarWig Player Com
Team sports communication system

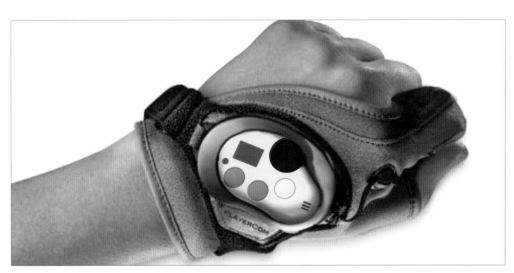

This product is a rugby coaching aid designed to allow a coach to talk directly to an athlete, or groups of athletes, while they are in training and playing environments. The product enables athletes to receive real-time feedback from the coach on performance and will enable the athlete to develop both technically and tactically.

The product will vastly improve both the amount and quality of specific feedback athletes will be able to receive, and will enable them to develop and improve at a faster rate than with conventional coaching methods.

My-Binh Ly
Industrial Design BSc

Relentless FretPlay Buddy
Fingerboard technique training device for guitarists

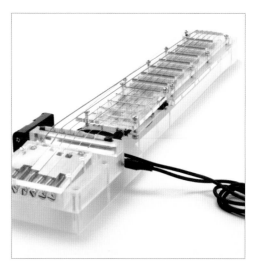

Playing an instrument requires dedication, determination and patience, but most importantly a lot of time devoted to practice. With the busy lifestyles of the present day this is something which many guitarists lack.

Resolving the physical difficulties faced when developing co-ordination and technique in the fretting hand allows this product to give the user a realistic practice experience to exercise their finger-work.

Empowering them with the freedom to practice at a level of progression to suit them, with the flexibility to practice more frequently when without their guitar. Assisting their long term goal of becoming a more accomplished player.

Alex McCarthy
Industrial Design & Technology BA

Extreme Cold Weather Face Mask
Protection against adverse conditions of extreme arctic and mountaineering exploration

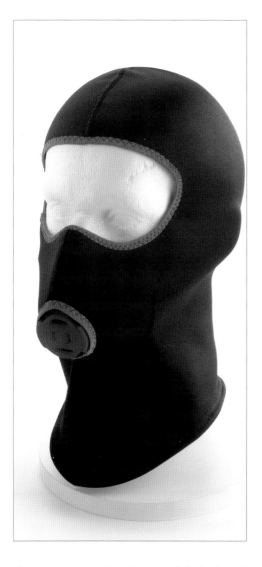
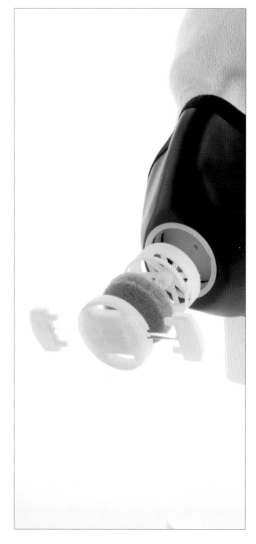

The extreme weather face mask is designed to tackle adverse conditions in extreme cold weather climates. The mask tackles all major inflictions such as frostbite, hypothermia and cold air-induced illnesses, whilst allowing the user to remain active and comfortable. The face mask utilises a breathing unit which regulates the temperature of the air breathed as a means of tackling lowering body temperature and cold air-induced illnesses. An important feature of the mask is its ability to bridge a variety of applications, allowing the mask to be used during periods of heavy physical exertion and also prolonged periods of being inactive.

Sam Mclintock

Product Design Engineering BSc

OmniGYM Detachable Barbell

Removable barbell for a new compact and folding home multigym

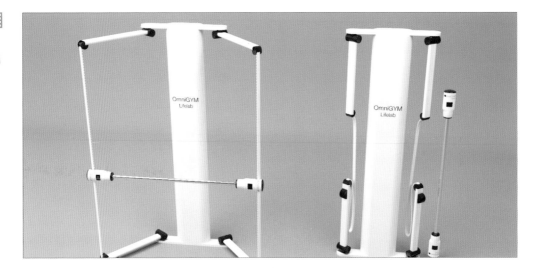

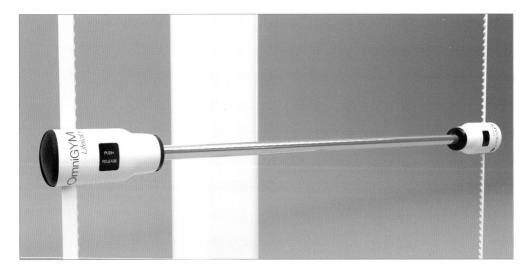

This was developed with Lifelab Innovations Ltd, a Brunel University spin-out company.

Strength training of large muscle groups with freeweights provides significant health benefits, particularly for older users. The Omnigym concept enables, for the first time, the use of a barbell, making freeweight exercises possible. eg deadlifts and squats.

The bar is attached to vertical belts, which are connected to the resistance mechanism. Additionally, the bar can be removed, allowing other exercises to be undertaken.

Importantly, the ability to fold the Omnigym into a compact form will save considerable space in the home when it is not in use.

PROXIM
Free standing architectural lounge light

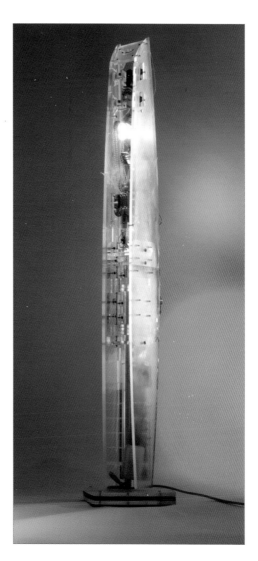

Proxim is a free-standing architectural style lounge light that provides ambient, mood and task lighting.

All the lighting controls are operated by the non-touch sensors near the top of the product. The coloured lights, white light combination, coloured light angle and the angle of the reading lamp are all adjustable.

Gary Mitchell
Product Design BSc

Philips HQ7390
Limited Edition AT&T Williams Shaver

Artwork for the Philips HQ7390 was produced as a part of Philips's sponsorship with the AT&T Williams team during my 12 month design placement at WilliamsF1 Engineering Ltd. The design was developed to encapsulate the race team brand, whilst creating a platform for Philips and the other partners of the race team to increase their exposure to, and association with, AT&T Williams.

My involvement at WilliamsF1 Engineering Ltd also included the branding of the race team environment, producing visualisations for current and potential sponsors and creating artwork for licensed products.

The Philips HQ7390 shaver is currently sold internationally.

Victoria Monks
Industrial Design BSc

Adapt to Life
Designing the product architecture of a notebook adapter

Notebooks are designed for convenience when travelling. However there has been little development and few innovations to the adapter. The project outline is addressing the cable management of a Notebook adapter. The design combines easy portability with a cable management system. The design ensures that the cable does not get tangled when being packed away.

The target market of this product is the business user that is always 'on-the-go' and dependent upon their Notebook as a place of work. It is compact and self contained, making it the ultimate travelling companion.

Mark Montgomerie
Industrial Design & Technology BA

All-in-One Ergonomic Stand + Case
An all-in-one ergonomic laptop bag and lap holder

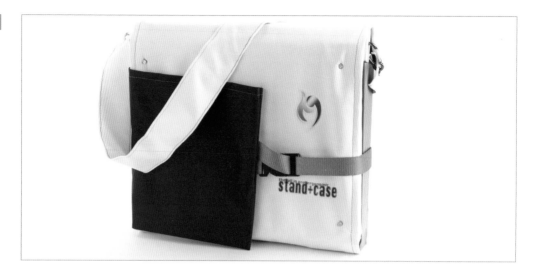

The use of the laptop on the lap creates problems; the laptop is not stable, making it very susceptible to damage. It is not comfortable to use for the user and while on the lap or any soft surface, the flow of hot air is constricted and builds up in the laptop causing further discomfort and damage.

This product solves these issues by the laptop residing permanently in an air cushioned carry case, whilst being easily accessible on the lap. The bag folds out to become a stable stand that promotes comfort and a natural posture whilst channelling heat away from the laptop.

Damon Murray-Morrish

Industrial Design & Technology BA

The Innovative Travel Case

A retracting wheeled self weighing travel case

This project is aimed at solving existing problems with current products within the luggage industry. It was inspired by problems experienced during air travel in particular. This re-design of the travel case addresses two main issues. Firstly the case incorporates a retracting set of wheels that fold up inside the case. This means that unlike current products, the wheels are less susceptible to being damaged when the case is in use for anything other than wheeled motion. Secondly, the Innovative Travel Case design features self weighing technology that allows the user to weigh their case before checking their bag.

Matthew Nourse
Product Design Engineering BSc

Variable Beam Width LED Lamp
An architectural lamp with variable beam angle

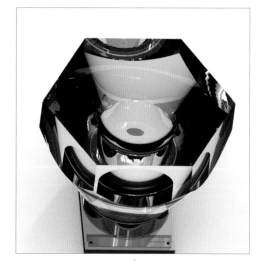

This project is the journey of thought from the idea of an environmentally friendly light source, using light emitting diodes to their best effect, which can also alter its beam width mechanically.

A year spent immersed in the world of professional architectural lighting illustrated a definite need for this product. Many companies have tried to achieve this with different light sources but with varied success. This product has been designed with their successes and failures in mind to create a better product, but also one that lighting designers will appreciate and specify.

Patrick O'Donoghue
Product Design BSc

Chimey
Interactive indoor wind chimes

This installation reacts to people as they walk past by playing a different note depending on the distance they are from Chimey. By adding a third dimension to this well recognised instrument, a unique ambiance is created, which constantly changes in sync with the general atmosphere of a space.

With a retail price of £120, Chimey is aimed at large crowded areas such as shopping centres to create a welcoming entrance or an engaging chill out area. In today's stressful society, it endeavours to help people discover a relaxing habitat in a familiar and playful way.

Nital Patel
Industrial Design BSc

Glimpse
An effective, easy-to-use and instant eye medication dispenser

It is estimated that over 70 million people around the world are affected by glaucoma. If untreated it can lead to partial visual impairment or even complete loss of vision. The main form of treatment is usually via administering eye drops, which have to be taken for life.

The method of administering eye drops is one that has not changed for many years. A user centred approach allowed for a thorough understanding of the limitations; dexterity, navigation and time were all highlighted as key problem areas with aged patients. Taking inspiration from the Tonometry – 'Puff of air' - test for glaucoma. Glimpse is designed to allow the user to administer a portioned 'one-drop' equivalent as a light mist into the eye.

Frederic Perry Phillips
Industrial Design & Technology BA

Fire Guardian
Home fire prevention and fire repulsion system

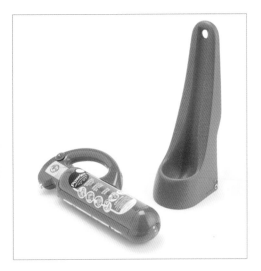

Fire alarms and fire extinguishers have some key problem. Fire alarms for example have a high failure rate due to users not replacing or changing the battery which can result in death in a case of fire. Portable fire extinguishers are not found in many households and are sometimes misplaced and difficult to use making them useless when they are needed. Fire Guardian aims to solve these issues at a systems level. It uses a radio-linked fire sensing unit and clever extinguisher that has built in intelligence such as a rescue beacon and LED lighting which can be used for escaping from a home.

Computer Numerically Controlled (CNC) systems are heavily used in the design process. One of the theories about the next manufacturing superpower is that it will be influenced by customisation, with the help of 3D printing and a whole range of other CNC rapid prototyping units. The project is aimed at youngsters who are studying design and technology at school, to enable them to have a better understanding of CNC machines. It uses a very simple computer package with different unit attachments; from a pencil to a router, making it safe to use. It can even be transformed into a full CNC router.

Pedro Pineda
Industrial Design & Technology BA

Fly Your Own Body
A timeless research and development

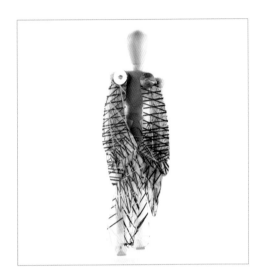

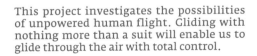

This project investigates the possibilities of unpowered human flight. Gliding with nothing more than a suit will enable us to glide through the air with total control.

Inspired by birds, this wing-suit makes use of bio-mimicry studies and the research and development of centuries of evolution. This natural knowledge is combined with current material findings and wing-suit's aeronautics to improve the flying characteristics already achieved by modern wing-suits.

While this may not be the final solution, it brings us one step closer to a timeless dream; human flight

Ed Powys
Industrial Design & Technology BA

TRAP EASE
Emergency quick release sailing trapeze hook

This project was to design and prototype a sailing trapeze hook that can be released from the sailors harness in case of an emergency situation.

For sailors of all abilities there is a risk of drowning by entrapment and the main reason for this is the trapeze hook, due to its protrusive nature and tendency to snag.

On average two people die a year from trapeze hook related incidents, in addition to many close calls.

The project aims to give peace of mind to sailors and has the potential to not only save lives but also tobecome a successfully marketed product.

Esteban Schunemann

Industrial Design & Technology BA

Scalectrix Race Engineer

Slot car racing from the point of view of the race engineer

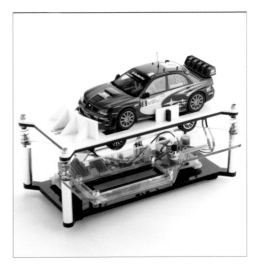

The race engineer is one of the most important roles in any racing team. This project embodies the role of the race engineer using embedded systems.

The player plans what speed the car must maintain in different places on the track using tags the scalectrix car can read, then the player can decide on the fuel levels for the car and the number of pit stops to develop a strategy in order to win against the other competitors.

Factors such as engine and gearbox failures also play a part in deciding if the player wins or loses the race, so the player must also keep an eye on the telemetry of the car.

Eden Smith
Virtual Product Design BSc

BIObelt
Abdominal training belt

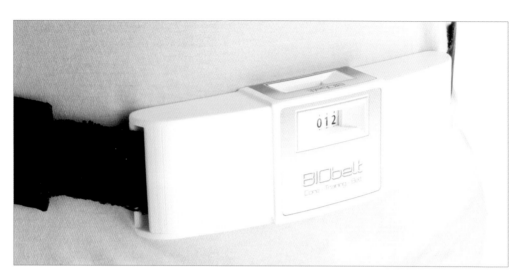

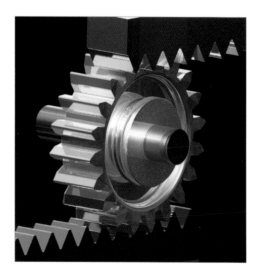

BIObelt is a concept formulated by LifeLab Innovations Ltd, a health and lifestyle innovation and Brunel University spin-out company. The BIObelt facilitates effective and safe abdominal exercise, by giving the user instantaneous feedback of abdominal muscle activation, enabling unprecedented levels of abdominal muscle contraction and training efficacy.

This project develops the concept to a stage where it can be mass manufactured. The process has included production of working prototypes, demonstrating the mechanics and proposed aesthetics of the product. In the second quarter of 2009, LifeLab will approach a leading American company with the aim of licensing the BIObelt.

Chloe Underhill

Industrial Design BSc

Composite Ball Valve

New uses for composite materials within aerospace applications

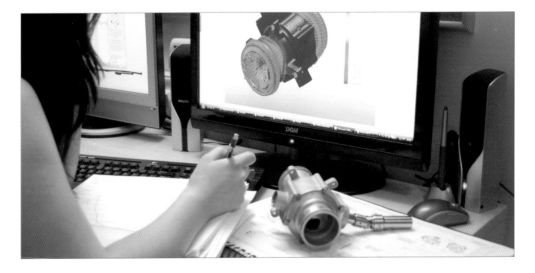

The Composite Ball Valve project is an investigation into the use of advanced composite materials in fuel system components in an effort to improve the eco-efficiency of future aircraft.

This research and development project aims to exploit the benefits of advanced composites. A successful example is the A380 which "uses composite materials in its wings, which helps enable a 17% lower fuel use per passenger than comparable aircraft." (Edwards, 2008).

Low mass, high strength composite materials offer significant fuel savings, greater payload and efficiency as well as possibilities for part integration and reduced manufacture and assembly time.

Rhys Welsh
Industrial Design & Technology BA

id+
Survival tool for today's office environment

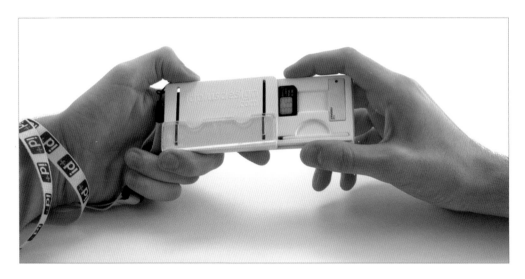

Id+ is a storage device specifically designed for business tools. Functions the product offer include ID Card Holder, Business Card Holder, pen, USB memory stick and a SIM card.

The objective is to target large corporations, governmental organisations and international companies. Daily hassles are frequent throughout the working day; so the product aims to reduce unnecessary tasks in the office. The intention is to increase productivity, security and reduce stress. Usability is important as it will be used by employees during office hours. This innovative design has no obvious competitors which can offer the same functionality.

David Michael Wood

Industrial Design & Technology BA

Freedom Shopping Trolley

Lightweight collapsible personal shopping trolley with integrated child seat

The product aims to allow shoppers more freedom by giving them their own personal trolley with improved steering and child seating facilities that can be easily collapsed when not in use. Furthermore it also allows users to make purchases from more than one shop without having to return their trolley which reduces repeat shopping trips. The insulated food storage facility also enables shoppers to preserve their food for a longer period of time whilst travelling to their final destination. The Cordura fabric basket also allows for easy cleaning and maintenance.

Brunel Racing

Brunel University Formula Student Race Team

Brunel Racing consists of six masters and a selection of third year mechanical engineering students. The team has competed in Formula Student competitions every year since it was established in 1999, producing a new car every year. Taking the cars to numerous locations worldwide, including the Silverstone and Hockenheim Grand Prix circuits.

For the purpose of the Formula Student competition, students are to assume that a manufacturing firm has engaged them to produce a prototype car for evaluation, and that the intended sales market is the non professional weekend autocross or sprint racer.

The design of every Brunel Racing car begins at the start of the academic year in September, with a design theme being decided upon by team management, who then offer guidance to the designers.

BR-9

BR-9 was the 9th car from Brunel Racing, and competed at Formula Student competitions in Great Britain and Germany.

The main design goals of BR-9 were to make the car smaller, lighter and lower than the team's previous car. In 2008, emphasis was placed on simplicity and reliability, rather than intricate systems deemed unnecessary by the team.

BR-9 weighs only 265kg, and its compact overall dimensions mean it can be easily transported to events, making the car an ideal choice for weekend or hobby autocross drivers.

It was designed with usability and maintenance in mind, as a result, most parts are easily serviced by the user. For example, the engine can be changed in an hour thanks to the detachable chassis rear-end. In addition to the ease of servicing, many of the car's setup variables can be adjusted by the user. Engine parameters can also be monitored and defined via BR-9's MoTeC ECU, by connecting a computer to the diagnostic port of the car.

Main Technical Features

The car has been tuned to produce a peak power output of 65bhp - equivalent to 245bhp per tonne, and a peak torque of 42Nm. It reaches 75mph from a standing start in 5s.

BR-9 uses a 600cc Yamaha R6 motorcycle engine, driving the rear wheels via a chain and a limited slip differential. The engine intake and exhaust are both bespoke parts designed by the team.

For optimum handling and grip, BR-9 employs double-wishbone suspension at the front and rear. Wheel camber and toe in/out are adjustable by the user, as are ride height, roll stiffness and rebound rate. Suspension springs are also easily interchangeable, as a result of the car's centre of gravity is just below 250mm off the ground, minimising body roll.

BR-9 is designed to accommodate drivers of all shapes and sizes, with the seat moulded to the driver's body shape. In order to take into account the lengths of different drivers' legs, the pedal box is mounted on a sliding rail. For maximum driver safety, a full five-point harness and arm restraints are fitted to the cockpit.

The steering wheel features a quick-release system, allowing easy access to the car. Brake bias is adjustable between the front and rear using a balance bar fitted to the pedal box.

As BR-9 is designed primarily for narrow, winding courses, aerodynamic devices do not feature heavily in its specification. However, its nose-cone, sidepods and under-tray have all been cohesively designed to keep drag to an absolute minimum.

BR-9 is styled with a classic aesthetic that harks back to the 'glory days' of motorsport, its colour scheme echoing that of Colin Chapman's classic Lotus F1 cars. The trailing edge of the sidepods features a small silhouette of Isambard Kingdom Brunel, the great British engineer from whom the university takes its name, offering a contrast to the modern technology beneath its skin.

BR-X

BR-X, Brunel Racing's 10th Formula Student entry, will be racing at competitions in Summer 2009.

The design aims for the 2009 car are to greatly reduce weight when compared to the BR-9, while still maintaining a simple, reliable and well-engineered product.

BRUNEL RACING

Team Details

Michael Allen Team Principal
Nick John Marketing & Drivetrain Manager
Rich Drury Design & Aero Manager
Jane Mackay Unsprung Manager
Andy Tomlin Chassis & Controls Manager
Dave Townson Powertrain Manager

Brunel X-team

An electric motorcycle for the Isle of Man TTXGP competition

BX-09 is Brunel X-team's entry to the 2009 Time Trials Xtreme Grand Prix (TTXGP), the first zero emissions motorcycle race. It is held alongside the prestigious Tourist Trophy (TT) at the Isle of Man circuit. Consisting of 1 lap of the 37.73 mile Mountain Course, the race pushes the limits of emerging technologies and provides the perfect platform to showcase the ideas and innovations of the team.

The team has used a Triumph Daytona 675 donated to them as a donor vehicle for reference and minor ancillaries. Major aspects of the motorcycle have been analysed, redesigned and tested to adhere to the rules of the competition and optimise performance.

Analysis Of The Problem

Being such a unique and notoriously challenging circuit, great importance was placed on track analysis to ensure a complete understanding of the rigors placed upon the bike in terms of power requirements and handling. The maximum velocities, track elevation changes, corner radii and subsequent lean angles were studied at over 300 points around the track. From this a true representation of the course and the required setup of BX-09 has been determined.

Following circuit analysis, an entire "throttle to road" simulation was produced in Mathworks Matlab/Simulink R2008a to precisely calculate the power requirements for the race. Calculations included the effects of rolling resistance, aerodynamic drag and drivetrain losses to best represent the race conditions. From this simulation an ideal power source was identified as well as the optimal battery pack configuration. It also allowed optimisation of the final drive ratios allowing the best compromise of acceleration and maximum velocity.

The distribution of mass and its effect on the stability and handling of BX-09 was considered throughout the design process. Once the chassis geometry was fixed it could be ensured that the centre of mass was optimally placed by careful location of the powertrain so as not to greatly differ from the original donor bike. It was also made sure that the ability of the front and rear suspension and maximum lean angle of the bike were not impinged upon.

Design and Creation of BX-09

One of the biggest challenges of this project was to house the lithium-ion cells required to get the bike around the course at a competitive speed. Drawing upon the findings of the vehicle dynamics study, cells were located in specific areas so that the centre of gravity, and mass distribution, was kept similar to that of the original Daytona 675.

When using an electric powertrain, there is a heavy dependence upon the control systems to ensure that not only the powertrain operates optimally, but also to make riding the bike as close to a conventional motorcycle as possible. Therefore, it has been a key design criterion of BX-09 to incorporate as much adjustability and tuning into the control system as possible.

The flexibility afforded by the Agni motor's power characteristics allows use of a single gear direct drive output. This is run from the motor through a bespoke AP Racing clutch to allow complete disconnection of drive to the rear wheel in the event of a powertrain failure. Special attention was paid to improving the overall performance of the standard Agni motor through lightweighting and advanced tuning.

BX-09 Specifications

Drivetrain
- Agni Motor
- Bespoke AP Dry Single Plate Clutch
- 520E Chain Upgrade
- Adjustable Gearing Ratio

Power Source
- LiFebatt Lithium-ion XPS Prototype Cells
- 72 V, 480 A System

Top Speed 100 mph +
0-60 mph 4 seconds
Torque 60Nm
Mass 220 kg

Team Details

James Owen Team Principal and Powertrain
Dafydd Broom Powertrain
Jamie McCombe Vehicle Dynamicist
Thomas Pegg Chassis

Project Scorpion

Regenerative vibration control for commercial engines

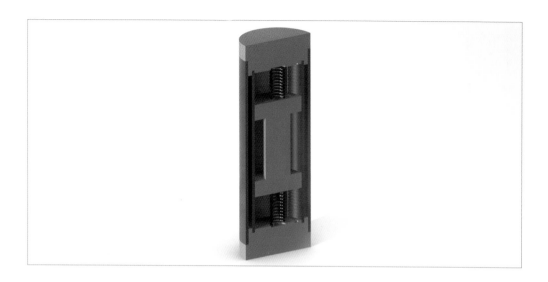

Increasingly stringent working regulations forces many companies to seek cost effective solutions to reducing noise and vibration, especially when workers may be operating plant for hours on end. Active and semi-active vibration control systems have been a common feature of luxury cars for some years; yet despite performing well tend to be overly complex and expensive to fit as standard on most commercial vehicles. An opportunity exists to develop a simple system designed for larger, more robust diesel powered vehicles. A vibration absorber, which isolates vibration through a system of sprung masses, provides an advantage over conventional engine mounts it they can easily be retrofitted to existing equipment.

Mass damping systems are not new, but using this principle to actively control the vibration transmissibility over a range of frequencies is something that has never been tried before. Electro-mechanical regulation of the kinematic properties of the sprung mass allows an active control scheme to be applied to a previously passive system. Because the device is working to absorb the vibration energy to which it is subjected; an induced voltage should always be greater than the voltage required to regulate the sprung mass, therefore there should always be a positive electrical energy output from the device. This resultant power could be used to charge the vehicle battery, or power auxiliary systems. The construction of the device has been optimised to make it as efficient as possible.

High performance springs support a special nickel-steel mass, which has very low magnetic impedance, and the Neodymium magnets at the heart of the device are the most powerful on the market. The free and fast movement of components is ensured through the use of low friction materials, which eliminate the requirement for oil lubrication and extend maintenance intervals. The unit is contained within a robust steel shell that also acts to amplify the effectiveness of the electro-mechanical control system.

IP has been secured, and Brunel's Commercialisation Office are now advising on future potential.

Team Details

Stephen Maclane Team Leader
Emil Tschepp Electro-Mechanical Design
Sarah Parkin Kinematic Simulation
Matthew Littlefield Testing Design

Open-Source Industrial Revolution

Alex Bygrave

In the late 1800's, great ideas facilitated by technological advancement gave rise to unprecedented global changes in society, infrastructure and economy. It appears that we may now be on the brink of the next industrial revolution.

The industrial revolution witnessed the rise of middle class industrialists and businessmen over the nobility. Cottage industries like textiles evolved, people no longer worked at home but found new opportunities for employment in factories and mills; giving rise to urbanisation and our modern cities says Martin Bridgstock in his book 'Science Society and Technology'. The introduction of the railway facilitated the transport of materials and goods, connected towns and cities, and enabled the masses to travel. Our current belief that a growing economy is a healthy economy, and economic growth is the normal state of affairs was born. According to 'The Industrial Revolution and British Society' by Patrick O'Brien, Britain saw the end of feudalism and the rise of capitalism.

Technological developments such as Watt's steam engine or the Spinning Jenny were the driving forces that enabled the first industrial revolution. However, the industrial revolution itself was a series of great ideas about manufacturing, the mechanisation of previously labour intensive tasks, organizing factories and trade unions says Steven Weber in his book, 'The Success of Open-Source'.

Current technological advancements in information technology and rapid manufacturing are set to provide a similar driving force behind the ideas of open-source design, mass customisation, crowdsourcing and co-design.

The Internet, widely acknowledged currently as 'Web 2.0' is "a system that harnesses collaborative intelligence" says O'Reilly. The Internet facilitates limitless communication and is increasingly being seen by many companies as a door to a wealth of intelligence. Crowdsourcing, which consists of harnessing the manpower available through the Internet has, according to Wired magazine, been used for many large successful projects including the genetic sequencing of E-coli, the construction of a map of the red planet by NASA for their Mars mission and project Guttenberg which has digitised 6000 books.

Co-Design, currently a thorny topic for many designers, involves designing with the leading edge consumer, or even allowing them to take the reins and become the designer, with the intention of better design led innovative solutions, says Clare Dowdy in Design Week. Although some designers disagree with this principle, Erich von Hippel argues in 'Democratising Innovation' that the popularity of mass customisation and studies on user product modification show the traditional 'one size fits all' approach is no longer good enough. Open-source design takes current concepts of user customisation to the next level and has the potential to turn the design world on its head.

The concept of open-source has existed for centuries, although it is nowadays most often associated with computer software such as the operating system Linux. Linux is not commercially protected, but exists in the public domain, it is free to download, and comes with the source code. In open-source software, users are encouraged to modify, improve and copy the source code, then redistribute it so that others can benefit from the improvements. These ideas go against the conventional notion of property; the right to exclude others from something that belongs to you.

The essence of open-source is the right to free access, copy and distribute. With easy to use 3D modelling software free to download from the Internet, this open-source approach has started to make an appearance in design. A small medical prosthetics company, The Open Prosthetics Project (OPP), uploaded 3D solid data for a prosthesis called the Trautman Hook. The OPP received many responses from the online community that led to major improvements in the design. Their aim is to provide innovations in the field of prosthetics and freely share the designs, making their creations available for anyone to use and build upon said New Scientists' Sam Boykin.

Rapid prototyping is a process where 3D objects are effectively printed directly from 3D CAD data, allowing for fast production of solid parts irrespective of their complexity. Rapid manufacture is the use of rapid prototype production methods to produce final parts or products and has already found its place in many areas of the medical, aerospace and product industries.

According to Design Week it has been predicted that domestic versions of the rapid manufacture machine will be available in 10 years. However, these are not likely to be cheap. That's why Adrian Bowyer and Vik Olliver of Bath University have developed RepRap, the Replicating Rapid-prototyper, an open-source rapid prototyping machine that can be built for €500. RepRap is currently capable of replicating 60% of itself (not including nuts and bolts). The plans, the bill of materials and code required to drive the machine can be downloaded from their web site (www. reprap.org). Their aim is to develop an open-source machine capable of complete self-replication, licensed under the General Public Licence and cheap enough to be accessible to small communities in the developing world. 'Theoretically,

there are no parts that cannot be made by RM processes, including circuitry and microchips' says Rapidform manager Martin Watmough in Design Week.

Does the traditional designer have a role in the future? Predicting the outcomes of the open-source industrial revolution is not an easy task; imagine trying to predict the effects of the first industrial revolution before it happened. However, it is fair to say that the open-source industrial revolution will have a, global, socio-economic and cultural impact, and designers are going to have to adapt.

With developments in how things are currently being designed such as mass customisation and co-design, the move towards open-source design is not just a one-off phenomenon but is here to stay. There are obviously huge problems that the concept of open-source design faces, the main one being who is liable? Rapid manufacture is already with us and in a few years the printing of whole products will be a reality. Give it a few more years and the fabricator will be as commonplace as the desk-jet printer. According to The Guardian, fabricating has been heralded as the technology that will bring down capitalism. That sounds like a big claim, but as the driving force behind the idea of open-source design, and with the internet playing a similar role as the railway in the mid 1800's maybe it is not so inconceivable. Capitalism has only really existed since the last industrial revolution anyway.

A full version of this essay is available at: www.madeinbrunel.com

Is Technology the Future?

Neil Willetts

The ability to create and use primitive tools first defined the human race as different from other species and allowed for the development of the race into what it is today. However, is technological advancement leading to the downfall of the human race? The Americas lost nearly three quarters of their large animals with the arrival of early man and his flint spear, and this has kick-started a trend of humans having an irreversible impact on the world around them.

Fast-forward to the modern age and people are used to technology as an integrated part of everyday life. People are connected to the world at large, while Web 2.0 allows users to immerse themselves in a whole other world of interaction. Thousands of friends on MySpace and hundreds of subscribers to your blog. But is this the best way to spend your time and money? Virtual friendships form and you can quickly access more knowledge than ever before, but where has the human interaction gone? We hear of young people who have committed crimes, often re-enacting experiences of the virtual world, but are advances in the technology to blame for the content being mimicked?

A six year old boy in Virginia, USA, stole his mother's car and attempted to drive to school after missing the bus. He claimed he learned to drive by playing Grand Theft Auto and Monster Truck Jam computer games. Who is to blame? Should the child have known not to steal the car? Should the mother not have allowed the child access to the game? Or could it be blamed on the computer games? In the case of a six year old boy, the blame surely cannot be placed on him, but for others that get overwhelmed with technology, should they know better or is the effect on them the responsibility of those who create the technology.

But what happens when the content is not governed by those who developed the technology? Is it fair to blame the Internet itself for its content? What about websites themselves? Web 2.0 is characterised by the dominance of user created content, such as Myspace, Facebook, Youtube and Flickr. Then again, the question of blame comes up with user generated content, and any possible impact that content may have on an impressionable user.

If a product or technology has been created to solve a problem, why should we not use it? You need to find information fast without wanting to move from your workstation, so you Google it; you want to buy that book for your other half without driving to town and going to the book shop, so you buy it on Amazon.co.uk; you want to eat whatever you want, as often as you want, without putting on a pound, so you take a pill for it.

In December 2007 The Guardian first reported on the GlaxoSmithKline (GSK) diet pill Alli, being available over the counter in the UK as early as 2008. Professor Alan Maryon-Davies, president of the faculty of public health, is worried that people will take the pills without receiving proper advice and support about dieting and exercise, stating "It's all too easy to pop a pill instead of making the lifestyle changes we need to keep our weight under control". Training packs will be given to pharmacists to ensure they do not give out the pill incorrectly and to be eligible for the pill you must have a body mass index (BMI, the measure that the World Health Organisation, uses to categorise weight levels) of over 28. One might argue the case of what happens for people whose BMI is 26 or 27 that want to lose weight, do they go the traditional route of healthy diet and exercise, or would they simply continue in their ways until their BMI is large enough to be allowed to buy the pill over the counter?

So why is exercise and a healthy well balanced diet not always the done thing? Is it the overweight person's fault that they are how they are, or has society allowed everyone to slow down and become complacent with the life we have? Once upon a time most people physically worked hard for a living, but it is now commonplace to go to school, go to university, get a job in an office and wait for retirement. But what could be done to re-stimulate people's minds, as they used to be by having such a varied week?

Irrespective of what possibilities the future might have in store for us, one thing is almost certain, society will care more for society. Recently there has been greater emphasis on well-being and human centred-ness in products. Nintendo are an obvious example of this with their 2005 DS and 2006 Wii games systems. The DS hosts a range of games that promote developing the brain, teaching you how to cook and build your own world with friends. The Wii focuses on physical interaction with the game, exercising whilst you play. It is not just the content and interaction that is changing, emotive connection with technology is becoming more important than the technology itself.

The current economic worldwide crisis has shown people on a large scale that actions have consequences, and this realisation will have an effect on how people choose to spend their time. If a society wants a change, then it will eventually happen. Health and happiness are more important to us now than ever, and as society is more vocal in what it wants designers and engineers will have to deliver.

So, what will happen in the years to come? No one knows exactly, but what we can say is that we have learned from recent years of excess and misdemeanour, and the focus will be on the user of the technology, not the technology itself.

A full version of this essay is available at: www.madeinbrunel.com.

sustainable

Designs and strategies which aim to reduce environmental impact.

As we become increasingly aware of the impact of mankind on the planet, greater focus is being placed on the way in which we live our lives. Designers and engineers have a responsibility to create products that are both sustainable and encourage a more sustainable lifestyle. This movement has brought about a new, more responsible type of thinking that is socially and environmentally aware. Concepts within this chapter embody Sustainable Thinking.

thinking

Future Concepts for Brita

To launch Brita into the setting of 2025, we have analysed the brand's core values, ethos and future forecasts to establish their position and role.

Following the recession, we are predicting that Brita's UK future customers may develop a 'post war mind set'. From day one Brita has had the focused vision: "A Brita product in every household."

We feel that this is wholly feasible providing Brita adapt to contextual issues. Our future direction for Brita is to concentrate on self-sufficiency within the home. The proposals will allow Brita to retain market dominance and continue to offer consumer benefits during the recovery from the 2008 financial crisis.

Madeleine Case
Industrial Design BSc

Home Sweet Home by Brita
Future concept for Brita

Project yourself forwards to 2025. We predict that after the credit crisis, people will have a 'post-war mindset'. Everyone will be doing their bit towards self sufficiency within the home. With most fruit and vegetables having limited harvest periods, making the most of a successful crop will be top priority. 'Home Sweet Home' is a preserve making machine.

Making chutneys and jams is a fun and creative process but also complicated, time consuming and messy. 'Home Sweet Home' will fit with the busy lifestyles of people but allow them to be efficient by producing home made preserves.

Daniel Coveney
Industrial Design & Technology BA

SWAP by Brita
Future concept for Brita

SWAP is an online product that provides users with a means to trade home grown vegetables and fruits with neighbouring houses and streets. SWAP is a kitchen-based product which may be found on the work surface or kitchen table. SWAP simply displays fruits and vegetables which are available in the local area. The product has a single scroll wheel at its centre which allows people to browse the available ingredients at their own leisure. If anything takes their fancy the supporting online Vegbay is where trading takes place. This product will help build healthy interactive communities.

Julien Hadley
Industrial Design BSc

My-oan by Brita
Future concept for Brita

A conceptual product for Brita that focuses on the well-being of its users. Monitoring the health of the plants prompts users to become more conscientious of their own health. Key elements of this project were in exploring user-product interactions and applying this to a contextual setting where Brita would not only provide people with products that maintain current brand attributes, but also drive for a more sustainable future.

Lucy Kay
Industrial Design BSc

Extracting Goodness by Brita
Future concept for Brita

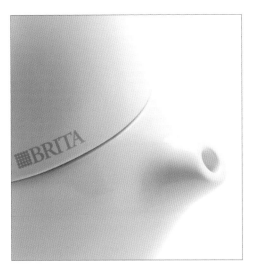

Brita are leaders in the field of water filtration and in the future they could be taking a further step to encourage their customers to further enhance healthier living.

The Brita aromatherapy oil extractor uses a combination of steam-distillation and supercritical CO_2 extraction technology. This is made possible by extracting the pure goodness that only comes from nature and turning it into something that is beneficial to our everyday lives.

Distillation is a process which involves extracting essential oils through the use of boiling water and steam. Flowers and petals can be reused to produce aromatherapy oils in minimal time. This is a step towards re-using waste in a beneficial and aromatic way.

Rebecca McGann
Industrial Design BSc

Butter up! by Brita
Future concept for Brita

An energy-free refrigeration system... the water inside the compact terracotta product evaporates, lowering the temperature of the porous terracotta and the butter that is stored upside-down inside.

The system is used to keep your home-churned butter cool and fresh, part of a range of products to provide a cool environment for the storage of other food; fresh fruit and vegetables, herbs and eggs.

This natural cooling solution is environmentally friendly, produced from sustainable and non-toxic materials.

Future Concepts for Green & Black's

Indulgence is an essential quality at Green and Black's. Whether they make chocolate, picnicware, jewellery or ambient lighting, the delicate balance between excellence and principles is crucial to their success.

These luxurious, ethical and environmentally friendly products are targeted at current Green & Black's customers.

The ranges encourage friends and families to spend time together, enjoying each other's company and enhancing their relationships and the quality of their lives.

Jamie Foxen
Industrial Design BSc

Green & Black's Ethical Jewellery
Future concept for Green & Black's

Luxury is changing. In the future our 'everyday luxuries' will become more guilty pleasures; socially and even legislatively. Our future luxuries will also be indulgent as well as environmentally and ethically sound.

This symbolic jewellery set strengthens the bond between you and someone special. It is hand crafted from the highest quality sustainably managed wood, from ethically sourced Carrara marble and from panned gold. Green & Black's cares for cultural craft identity, sustainable materials and ethical practices, allowing you to indulge with those that you care for.

Yasmin Idris
Industrial Design BSc

Green & Black's Nourishment
Future concept for Green & Black's

Green and Black's Nourishment for the soul has been designed for the cash rich, time poor, customer. This product aims to optimise the quality of leisure time which is in itself an indulgence for this customer profile, by electronically sensing mobile signals and various other external interferences within the living room vicinity, and communicating their undesired presence through the intensity of light. This sumptious warning system creates an invaluable oasis of calm within one's home and providing countless opportunities for social enhancement, without determent to the environment.

Anna West
Industrial Design BSc

Green & Black's Wine Insulator
Future concept for Green & Black's

Indulgence is changing. People will continue to want the luxuries of the past, but might feel pressured by environmental demands of the future. Green & Black's provide quality products to satisfy desires whilst removing environmental pressures.

The Green & Black's wine insulator is made from natural and organic fabrics, maintaining the wine at the optimum temperature. It is fairly traded and environmentally friendly for guilt free luxury.

What could be more indulgent than taking a picnic to a summer concert, or to the park, enjoying fine wine with family and friends?

Future Concepts for Weleda

Weleda sees the universe as an integrated whole. This was the personal philosophy of Rudolf Steiner, the company's founder, more than 80 years ago. Weleda passionately believe that health is much more than a lack of disease, but an integrated state of physical, mental, social and spiritual wellbeing.

Weleda's research of a health and well-being takes us back to the essence of the company, the four basic elements that are embedded in our being; Earth, Wind, Fire and Water. As each of these elements are connected to how the body works, these products focus on finding new ways of improving the consumers' lives with natural and positive influences, supporting the lifestyle of a "health conscious" individual.

Michael Abate
Industrial Design BSc

Weleda Flow
Future concept for Weleda

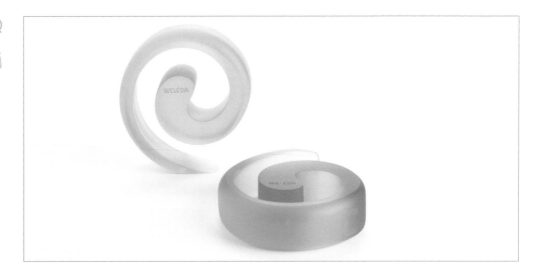

Flow is inspired by air and the way it moves. The product improves blood circulation by gentle squeezing in the palm of the hand. This eases conditions like Reynaud's disease, which results in constriction of the blood vessels to the extremities, as well as other blood circulation problems.

Circulatory problems are quite common and Weleda believe that through correct implementation, medication can serve as a supporting option with natural excercise products such as Flow.

Flow's two interconnecting parts fit perfectly together; the assembled unit sits upright.

Pedro Pineda
Industrial Design & Technology BA

Weleda Mutka
Future concept for Weleda

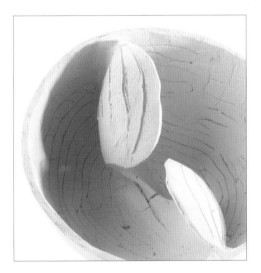

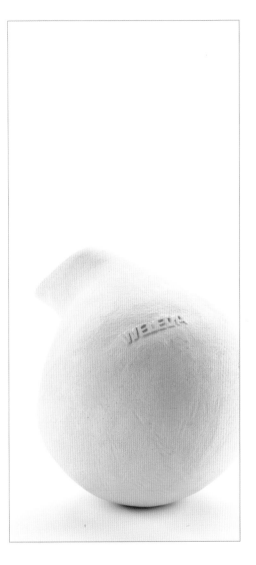

Weleda believe in strengthening the human being by supporting the inner healing tendencies and qualities of the individual. By using water, Weleda brings natural flow and rhythm which is inherent in it to our bodies. Mutka helps to revitalize the water and maintain its freshness at home. The revitalization depends on the rhythmic use and the internal structural form through which the water flows. Mutka has the perfect proportions so that its inner geometry will shape the water when it flows through its forms. At the same time the natural properties of the white terracotta used to make Mutka, self regulates its temperature relating to the environment to keep the water constantly fresh.

Kunal Sethi
Industrial Design BSc

Weleda Pear
Future concept for Weleda

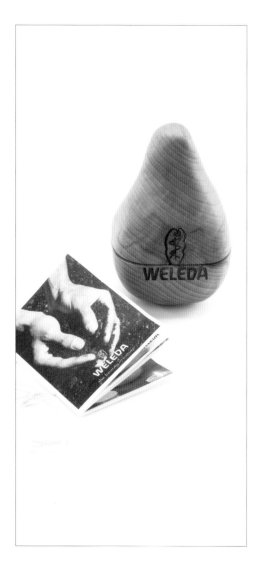

Our muscles endure a lot of wear and tear. The Weleda Pear allows for a self-massage using the different sized rolling balls to give a deep tissue or light relaxing massage. Massaging provides health benefits such as soothing chronic joint and muscle pain, battling fatigue, easing stress and combating depression. Using the extensive Weleda oil range, the Pear can also provide an oil massage, nourishing, moisturising and keeping the skin happy.

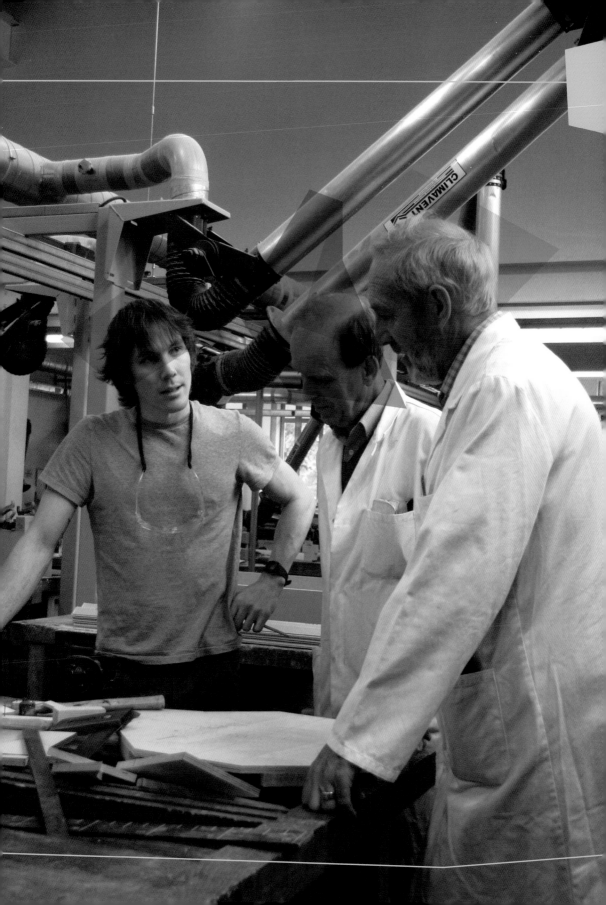

Reclaiming our Politics

Who're You Calling Apathetic...?

Elizabeth Baines

If present day politicians are to be believed, we live in an era of popular apathy. Today's youth make up the 'who cares?' generation. With little thought for society, and even less for politics, they sit around playing on Playstations, watching Sky and communicating on Facebook.

Don't they?

From the depths of modern youth culture, something exciting is happening, something creative and passionate. A generation of young people have grown up with the threat of climate change hanging ominously over their heads. Time and again, they have been told that the problem faced is unparalleled, urgent and potentially catastrophic. They have been warned of the pressing need to act now. Yet, just as this emerging generation is beginning to appreciate the scale and extent of global warming, so they are becoming increasingly aware of the emptiness of government rhetoric and promises to safeguard the environment.

The political system, whilst warning of environmental disaster, continues to propagate the arrangements which led to this state of affairs. With the degradation of our climate and the failure of our financial systems, the deep rooted cracks we knew were eating away at the foundations of our socio-political system have finally begun to break through the surface.

Yet, encouraged by government and industry, our society continues to cling onto a false and deceptive dream. To enshrine the capitalist illusion, the powers that be have done their utmost to ensure that alternative discourses are shut out. In today's politics, subtle processes of manipulation and coercion have led to the restriction and confining of channels for debate. Creative spaces have been lost in the drive towards efficiency, high market productivity and economic growth.

In a world where the language of the free market has reigned supreme for decades, decisions are made on the basis of their market value, largely irrespective of their social or environmental cost. Space has become capital, time has become money. Yet in an age where the only language understood in the political arena is capitalist discourse, where are the political, social or intellectual spaces for the expression of alternative views? Where can individuals propose innovative ideas which are not restricted by mainstream intellectual frameworks?

The spaces in which we live, work and socialise reflect the ideologies we have grown up with, and the aspirations we hold within. In modern society, the images which have come to dominate represent the capitalist ideals of modernity and unperturbed progress. Yet grass roots activism is posing an increasing challenge to these ideals.

Where political debates suffocate and stifle creativity, grass roots activist groups such as Plane Stupid, Climate Camp, Climate Rush, or The Coal Hole offer a shared space for innovative and creative thinking. Those engaged in these groups are not lobbying for business interests.

They are not politicians, although they have great political knowledge. They are there because they see so much of what is wrong and are determined to put it right. These people know what the future has in store if we fail to act decisively on climate change. They are acting out of a sense of responsibility
to both the planet and future generations.

Where the government largely refuses debate which places issues of wealth creation, financial gain and exponential growth anywhere but in the highest rank, debates within activist circles disregard politics' hierarchy of topics. Creativity occurs as a result of a frustration with traditional ways of thinking which have proven destructive and exclusive. Activism involves innovative channels of communication which are based on maximising input from as many people as possible. Debates are not about gaining power, status, or maximising financial rewards; indeed they are often focused on quite the opposite.

Those involved in activism are therefore constantly creating spaces in which to discuss new ideas, alternative solutions and inspired ways in which to perceive space and place. The rising trend of high profile protests, such as the Climate Camp at Kingsnorth power station and the shutting down of Stansted Airport by Plane Stupid, pay testament to the next generation's desire for change. Grass roots groups such as Plane Stupid, who oppose airport expansion and short haul flights, are indirectly encouraging different approaches to time and distance. If globalisation is founded on the metaphorical shrinking of time and space, changing travel habits means reassessing one's time agenda. Yet slowing down our travel does not mean a lower quality of life. Instead, the opposite is often true: air travel decreases our appreciation of time and space, of the specificity of place and the people and cultures within.

Whilst such campaigns are by no means exclusive to the younger generations of society, a growing number of those involved have not long left college. These activists are passionate and educated members of a growing faction of society which is looking towards a positive future. The spaces which this future occupies are communal and the land it inhabits is valuable not because of its economic worth, but because of its intrinsic beauty. This generation, having been brought up in an era of climate change, is increasingly aware of its responsibility to act. As activists, we are not only taking back our right to shape the spaces we inhabit and redefining the way we exist within these spaces. We are speaking truth to power, creating alternatives, and reclaiming our politics.

Elizabeth Baines
Plane Stupid

Cape Farewell
David Buckland

Working internationally, Cape Farewell bring artists, scientists and communicators together to stimulate the production of art founded in scientific research. Using creativity to innovate, we engage artists for their ability to evolve and amplify a creative language, communicating on a human scale the urgency of the global climate challenge. Cape Farewell is widely acknowledged to be the most significant sustained artistic response to climate change anywhere in the world.

We are an artist led organisation, created in 2001. Since the project began, we have invited artists to join science-led expeditions to the Arctic and to work with us on our ongoing programme of exhibitions and events. Cape Farewell has led seven expeditions to the High Arctic; the frontline of climate change including two youth voyages run in collaboration with the British Council. The ambition is to inspire those who have joined an expedition to respond creatively to the challenge of climate change. Through our expedition programme, we have engaged over 50 artists in the subject of climate including musicians KT Tunstall, Jarvis Cocker and Jonathan Dove, visual artists Antony Gormley, Gary Hume and Rachel Whiteread, choreographer Siobhan Davies, writers Ian McEwan and Vikram Seth, poet Lemn Sissay, playwright Suzan-Lori Parks and comedian Marcus Brigstocke.

From these expeditions has sprung an extraordinary body of artwork, ideas, images and media inspired by the interaction between the artists and the scientists working in the High Arctic and beyond. Our work continues to have a worldwide impact and has established our position as a pioneering force responding to the climate challenge. Cape Farewell has exhibited across the world, from Europe and North America, to Australia and the Far East. Our major exhibition, Art & Climate Change, created in partnership with the Natural History Museum in 2006, was most recently shown at the Miraikan Science & Technology Museum, Tokyo during the G8 Summit in Hokkaido 2008 and was opened by Sarah Brown, the wife of British Prime Minister, Gordon Brown.

Our exhibition programme also includes features such as panel discussions, art projections, sound installations, comedy and live music. These exhibitions are a chance to display the creative pieces that have emerged from time spent within our programme. In February 2009, we hosted Sublime Environments a Late at Tate event at the Tate Britain which featured, amongst other pieces, novelist Ian McEwan and Sunand Prasad (President of RIBA) talking publicly about their first hand experience of climate change.

The High Arctic, for a myriad of reasons, provides a place for real artistic investigation. It is on their journey to the world's tipping points that our artists and scientists begin their conversations, which lead to further research and production of pioneering new work. Each artist has found new and innovative ways to represent this extraordinary place and the implications of climate change.

We work with an eclectic group of artists, diverse in experience and expertise. Our invitations are always personal and made to artists who Cape Farewell trust and admire. We offer a unique route for artist development and every artist that has so far journeyed with Cape Farewell has been inspired to create work.

Climate change is a cultural issue that must move beyond scientific debate. Cape Farewell believes that artists have the ability to inspire a cultural shift necessary to face the challenge of climate change.

David Buckland
Cape Farewell

Cape Farewell has led seven expeditions
to the High Arctic since 2001. These have
inspired a growing body of artwork,
including ongoing exhibitions and events,
a film "Art from a Changing Arctic", co-
produced with the BBC, which has been
viewed by a global audience of over 12
million people, a major book "Burning Ice",
a CD "Arctic", by Max Eastley, educational
resources for GCSE Geography and Science,
and a UN award-winning website.

www.capefarewell.com

Trusting the Innovators

Joe Ferry

In a world that is constantly changing, companies have to instigate change just to stand still. For businesses to forge ahead of their competition, they have to move faster than the speed of change itself.

I know that this is easier said than done, as change within large organisations is usually greeted with fear or at best apprehension. But in order to progress faster and further than their competition, companies require enough bravery and capital to take risks and invest in innovation.

Good ideas can benefit a company whilst great innovations can command great returns. If the journey of discovery is navigated successfully, the benefits can be spectacular. Unfortunately, despite the odd apple falling and bath overflowing, innovative ideas don't generally come overnight. Being free to think, to allow innovative thinking when the outcome is unpredictable or unknown is a risk and an investment that world-class companies have to be prepared to take.

Innovative thinking is something we were all born with. Our innovative thoughts diminish when, at a fairly young age we are told to stop having our own ideas and taught to focus on remembering facts that have established themselves in the known world. We seldom educate people to go on a journey of discovery to use their imaginations to their full potential. This could be regrettable as we may now be fast approaching a time when it will not be the limitations of technologies, materials and scientific understandings that will prevent mankind's advancements; it will be the limitations of our own imaginations.

For us to create new journeys for our thoughts, it is sometimes helpful to question what we all consider to be the 'givens'. Let's not forget that at one stage in history it was a 'given' that the world was flat. Without challenging the 'givens' we cannot truly be innovative. Real innovation occurs when you don't know what the unknowns are and you embark on a journey to discover them. I know this may sound like a romantic notion only held by creative types and not welcomed by commerce, but it actually forms the basis for many innovative companies that see a massive return on their innovation investments.

To allow these ideas to see the light of day, there is one golden element that is required: you need support from the very top. There are many reasons to dismiss designs, to reject unresolved ideas that are full of risk and uncertainty. When the costs are mounting up and the timescales are running down, if there is no trust and support from above, the task of innovation can become virtually impossible.

Dismissing ideas because there are so many issues with making them work is usually the wrong strategy to take. I remember spending weeks staring at a project, when we knew we had optimised the product's space for two different functions, but didn't know how to achieve the transition between those spaces. At that stage, if we had given up due to all the well trodden criteria that you apply to these ideas telling you that it's unachievable, we would never have made the innovative leap that turned the idea from a good one to a great one. Instead we delivered great market share shifts, a good return on investment and millions of pounds in licensing agreements for the intellectual property of the innovation.

The key is not to give up when there
isn't an immediate solution but
to have the confidence that somewhere
there is a solution waiting to be discovered.

To deliver such innovative thinking needs
belief, leadership and innovators that
are valued within their company. In the
darkness of the future, when fear of the
unknown prevents it from becoming the
known, you have to believe in your leading
lights of innovation. I am certain that we
can discover anything, if we allow
the creative dreamers of the world
to keep on dreaming.

Joe Ferry
Head of Design
Virgin Atlantic Airways

Thinking of Design + the Recession

Chénay Nicole Williams

Depending on the perspective, some say that fashion has lost its way; others say fashion is finally developing as a business rather than an art. The differing views stem from the shift in the fashion industry—away from designer dictators and into a world of market research and consumer demand. The artistic designer brands of yesteryear seem to have fallen from grace and are clinging to their heritage whilst megabrands continue to rise.

As a society, we have moved into a lifestyle that is dictated by rampant consumption practices and the growth of fast/value fashion. Journalists are constantly commenting on the new age fashion consumer that happily floats between luxury brands and value fashion with little reverence for the conflicting concepts.

Consumers have come to expect a fast turnaround of high fashion into low priced garments. With faster and faster access to the latest runway trends, it would seem that fashion cycles are shortening and demand for new items is rising.

In her book, *Eco Chic*, author Sandy Black notes, "Relative to income, clothes are now far cheaper than they were a few decades ago. Clothing sales have increased by 60 percent in the last ten years. We now consume one third more clothing than even four years ago… and discard it after wearing just a few times or indeed, once."

Which leads to my current question – what impact does the current economic climate have on the creation and consumption of design?

From a financial perspective, retailers have experienced a decline in sales figures as compared to years past and projected sales increases for 2009. Retailers would have many believe that the industry is suffering and, in many ways, I am sure it is. But, I can't help but wonder if the financial downturn will actually have a positive effect on social practices.

In theory, as the world's economic situation worsens, consumers should place a greater importance on the quality of their purchased design products. Purchasing items that have longevity—items built to last. I would like to say that the days of rampant consumerism disappeared with the fall of the economy. And that maybe we will return to a time where we took care of our possessions and held onto items for years— where we believed in repairing and mending rather that disposing and replacing. I am not sure that this is actually the case—some may say it's just wishful thinking.

This is not to say that I am happy with the current economic state, but rather offering a question to the design community for deliberation. And with that, I also ask: how will this change occur – will designers pro-actively begin to create with these concepts in mind or will it be a design reaction to the fall in consumer spending? As we progress into the future I look forward to further observation of how design and the economy relate to one another.

Chénay Nicole Williams
Beyond the Valley Insight
Design and Branding Assistant

Brunel University Graduate, 2008

Inderpal Bhogal
Multimedia Technology & Design BSc

Recycle Me
A short animation on recycling at Coca Cola Enterprise

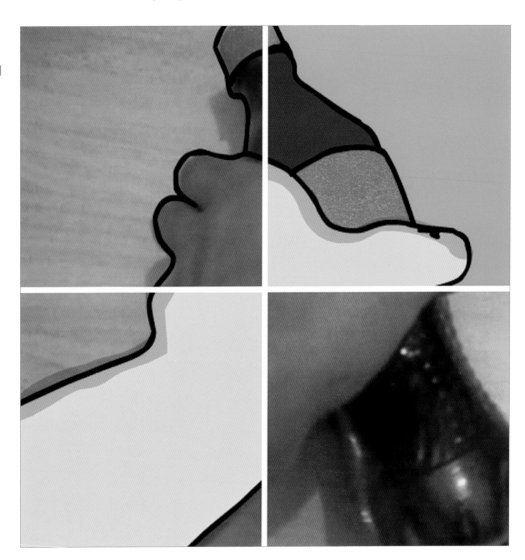

The aim of this project is to produce a 1-2 minute animation based around the work done by Coca-Cola Enterprise with regards to their recycling programme. The main focus within the recycling section will be around increasing the number of plastic PET bottles being recycled to ultimately reduce landfill.

The animation will be produced using Adobe Flash, with a style that has been developed through the early stages of the project. This animation can then be used on websites and in presentations to demonstrate the ongoing recycling activities within the company.

Christopher Bland
Industrial Design & Technology BA

Forget Me Watt
Automatic device which prevents standby waste from electrical products

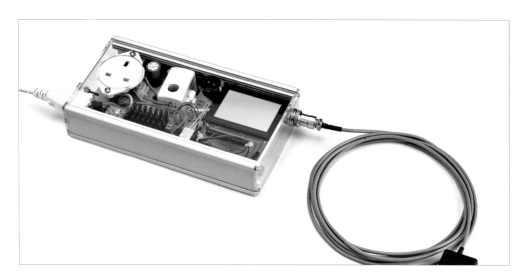

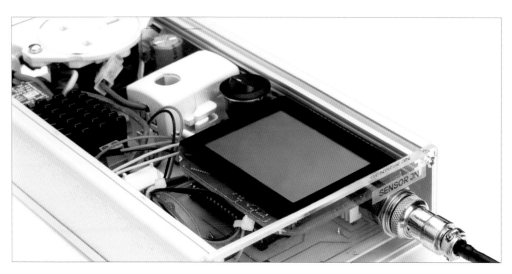

Leaving electrical products on standby can shorten their overall longevity and waste electricity. This device aims to tackle this issue by monitoring when the user is present and whether devices are actively on, or in standby. It is a fully automated system which can turn off devices in standby when not required and back on when the user is present and needs them. The device gives peace of mind to the user and is one less thing to worry about in everyday life whilst being more environmentally friendly.

Dominic Burton
Industrial Design BSc

Humanitarian Hearing Aid
Hearing Aid Designed to be Remanufactured from unused hearing aids

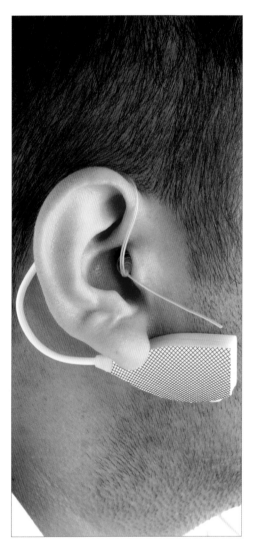

The Humanitarian Hearing Aid is designed to be remanufactured from unused, yet perfectly functional NHS hearing aids and distributed in less economically developed countries. The aim is for the hearing aid to be suitable for use straight after delivery with diagnosis and fitting carried out by the user whether or not they have a medical background.

It is specifically for high frequency noise induced hearing loss and Afghanistan was chosen as a territory to focus the design. The electronics will remain the same and the body has been redesigned to suit the climate and services of the destination country.

This project was supported by RNID.

Daniel Coveney
Industrial Design & Technology BA

Bottle Cutting Machine
Recycling glass bottles into usable drinking glasses

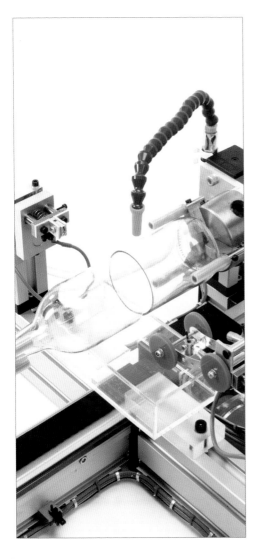

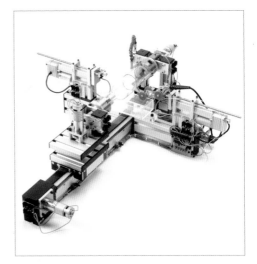

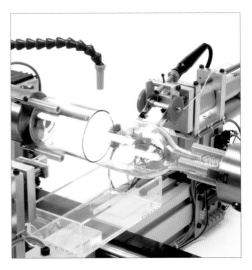

The aim of this project was to develop a process or method that would encourage more of the public to recycle and change the way domestic waste is viewed in the UK.

The outcome is a working prototype for a recycling vending machine concept. The machine converts empty glass bottles into usable drinking glasses. This may be found in places such as Supermarket lobbies. The user inserts an empty glass bottle and the machine divides it into two parts, disposes of the neck half to be recycled, and processes the bottom half into a drinking vessel.

Jamie Foxen
Industrial Design BSc

LED Colour Stability
Clear Light

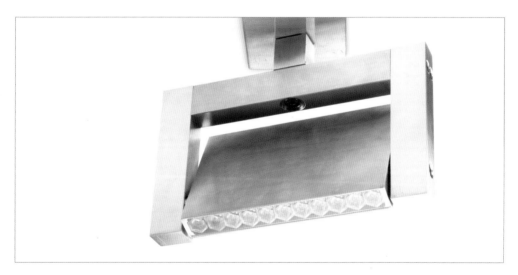

Multicoloured white LED lighting is the future. These light sources can approach 100% efficiency. Their environmental credentials are immense, however colour and luminous emittance instability renders them unsuitable for lighting applications.

This project developed a novel feedback system, resulting in one sensor providing precision CCT and illuminance in individual locations, independent of environmental interferences (e.g. sunlight) contained in an smart and efficient package. It allows the dynamic capabilities of a multicolour LED light source to be employed in a user-friendly and economical fashion. Further development could harness these properties for any size of environment. There are many possibilities for the number of LED light sources and their lighting applications.

Daniel Gray
Broadcast Media Design & Technology BSc

Journey Home
A motion graphics project to promote awareness of climate change

Environmental change has become a popular talking point with world leaders and global businesses quick to recognise the problem but slow to take action. Journey Home is a motion graphics piece that highlights the real environmental issues that face us today.

Created in a 2.5D style the piece follows the fortunes of a polar bear, recognised as being endangered because of climate change. The bear loses his home as it slowly melts away. He sets out on a journey across the world to find a new habitat and is forced to adapt to his new surroundings.

Aakrati Gupta
Product Design BSc

Flux
An emperical aerodynamic design for a solar race car

Aerodynamic perfection is the ultimate quest. The purpose of this project is to investigate and optimise the aerodynamic efficiency of a solar powered race car, similar to those, that compete in the World Solar Challenge in Australia every two years. The aim is to develop an empirical design i.e. an ideal aerodynamic car body shape with the lowest possible coefficient of friction considering various complex engineering factors and other limitations of solar power and energy consumption within vehicle design.

Tim Holley
Industrial Design BSc

Tio
Increasing children's awareness of energy consumption

Increasing the younger generation's awareness of energy consumption now will help to effect change in the future. A simple way to engage and educate them is to concentrate on lighting, which accounts for up to 15% of electricity use in the home.

Tio increases children's awareness of the energy their lights consume and the effect this has on the environment. Tio encourages children to turn lights off, and becomes more irritable the longer they are left on.

Information is sent to a computer by Tio, allowing energy use to be tracked over time. This engages children to make a personal contribution to reducing energy consumption.

Supported by Onzo.

Tim Holtom
Industrial Design & Technology BA

antARK
Build | Transport | Farm | Feed | Attack | Defend | Medicate | Communicate | Sing | Multiply

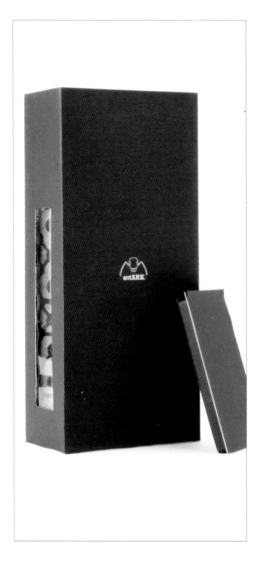

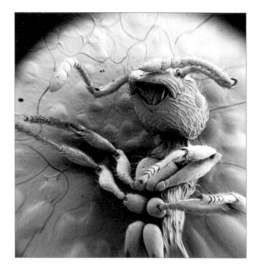

antARK is a modular formicarium that houses a colony of ants. Targeted at the nine and above age group, it aids the teaching of life-cycles, nutrient-cycles and photosynthesis.

No existing formicarium has yet been designed to nest a whole colony of ants, from the workers to the queen and all inbetween; the antARK does.

The first marketed formicarium has sold over 20 million items. antARK's modularity gives scope for add-on sections such as an aphid farm feeder, or a venus fly trap. The initial unit will be priced around £40.

If tended correctly, the queen ant could rule her colony for up to 29 years.

Lucy Kay
Industrial Design BSc

Flo
Aromatic room enhancer

A room fragrance enhancer, which senses and allows the user to adjust fragrance quality and quantity, when and how often they like. Flo utilises very efficient technology provided by Flowcap Ltd. This technology is proven to be far more efficient in diffusing fragrance than any commercial and electrical freshener in the market allowing it to be smaller, healthier and more desirable. Flo can add fragrance to any part of the home.

Robert Merriman
Industrial Design & Technology BA

Wind-Up Toothbrush
A spring powered wind-up toothbrush

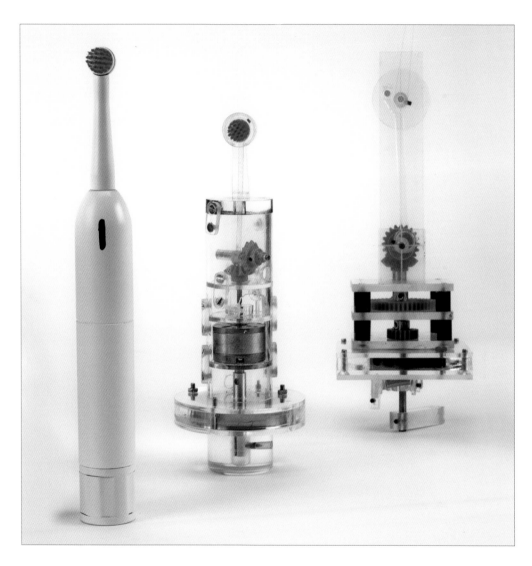

This product eradicates the electronic components of an electric toothbrush allowing it to be used anytime, anywhere without the concern of charging or finding a necessary power supply. The electronics have been replaced with a spring mechanism, wound up by the user. When the spring mechanism is released the brush moves like a conventional electric toothbrush.

This product incorporates the health benefits of an electric toothbrush which have been proven to increase plaque removal by 7% and reduce gum inflammation by 17% with the environmental benefits of removing the potentially harmful batteries and electricity wasting charging units.

Ainur Orazbayeva
Industrial Design BSc

'Vita-Drip' Subsurface Drip Irrigation (SDI)
Water saving irrigation product

Water crisis has become the reality for millions of people affecting them in different ways, among which hunger is one of the most shocking aspects. About 25,000 people die, daily, from hunger due to a shortage of water, preventing growth of crops.

'Vita-Drip' SDI is designed to make SDI technique accessible to many ordinary people around the world and to increase water productivity. The idea of SDI is to deliver an exact amount of water directly to the root zone of the plant drop by drop, which can cut water wastage via evaporation and leakage from present 60% to 0% of total used water. Simplicity and portablity of the product allow the user to irrigate larger areas and widely spaced crops without wasting any water.

Viral Patel
Multimedia Technology & Design BSc

Destroy the Blanket
Climate change campaign

Climate Change is here whether we like it or not. Affecting our climate and threatening our way of life.

The aim of the advert is to show the effects of Climate Change to the general public. The advert introduces the concept of the 'Greenhouse Blanket'. This 'Blanket' represents the greenhouse gases in the atmosphere, trapping the heat trying to escape from the earth. The advert shows this 'Blanket' in a visual way, trapping us in our everyday lives.

The end message of the advert urges the viewer to sign an online petition to help make a difference.

Annika Pugh
Industrial Design & Technology BA

Less
Packaging shower gel that reduces waste

Less is a new way of packaging shower gel. Its aim is to reduce natural resources used in manufacture of the product and the amount of material that is sent to landfill. It incorporates clearly visible metering to highlight the precise volume of shower gel has been used.

The shower gel is packaged in thin plastic pouches that are inserted into a roller mechanism that is secured to the bathroom wall. A dispenser is inserted into the base of the bag and shower gel can be dispensed by winding up the roller.

Robert Walsh
Industrial Design & Technology BA

Office Paper Recycling
Paper coating system

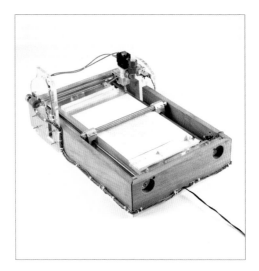

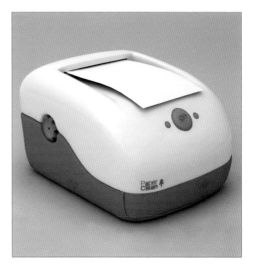

Paper usage in the UK accounts for 40% of all commercial and residential waste, with offices in London alone churning out over three and a quarter million tonnes of office and printing paper a year. This is a huge amount wasted, especially when 75% of paper in offices has a lifespan of less than a week and over 50% less than a day.

This project aims to increase the working lifespan of a piece office paper. In principle, the paper is coated in a solution that covers the printed or written content, providing a second use for the clean paper.

Alex Weldon

Industrial Design BSc

ECO DRIVE

Accelerator pedal attachment for safe and economic driving

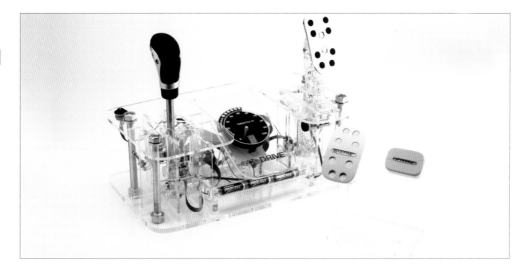

The project explores the use of tactile feedback as a medium for communicating with the driver, in an advisory based system that enhances the user's driving performance in terms of optimised fuel economy and improved safety.

Electronic components are embedded in an aftermarket accelerator pedal that wirelessly communicates with the car's on board diagnostic (OBD) port, vibrating signals are triggered through inefficient transmission, excessive acceleration and on exceeding a maximum speed limit. The project aims to provide a driving aid that enhances economy and safety without further distracting the driver, or removing control from them.

Taking the World Back from the Junkies
The Hitchhiker's Guide to Sustainable Design

Esteban Schunemann

How do we take the world back from the junkies??

Really, we can't because well, this in fact would entail some sort of sophisticated "matter transference-O-matic drive" as we would somehow need to take the world back from ourselves and still be in the world, almost like having the cake and eating it. Because current technology is far from developing such extraordinary machines that can solve the having the cake and eating it equation, we will have to opt for a much simpler solution, how do we stop being the junkies?

Some say the first step is to evaluate what we really need against what we really want. We have developed our technologies to improve our levels of comfort in life not quite understanding the consequences of the production and later disposal of the goods that make our lives so "rewarding".

In this process we have quite aptly managed to squeeze the less fortunate countries that produce most of the raw materials that we gorge ourselves with, leaving them in desperate need. Since this process started we also managed to set the now not so very strong foundations of an economy that would then help to sustain and encourage these patterns of consumerism. Also managing on the way to accumulate more than 80% of the world's wealth and leaving this less fortunate countries not only working for our comfort but also leaving them to share the remaining 20% of wealth. This relentless consumption is bound to produce waste that we didn't plan for and now we face an uphill struggle to change our living patterns and also try to convince the less fortunate to change them as well.

The world cannot continue to operate in such unsustainable ways, but steps are currently being taken to stop our wasteful addictions.

There are several books and articles that have recommendations and advice on green living (How to go carbon neutral, green living for dummies…) however most of these tend to have similar information. The most common message is: stop using fossil fuels, or at least reduce the amount! This can be achieved, but the main problem is the pattern of behaviour we have set for decades, and it doesn't help either that every day devices are designed to be left in standby, as they become more complex with more intricate programmes, it would be far easier if things just turned off when you told them to.

All these green living alternatives require the person performing them to make a conscious and active change in the way they think and live and not many are willing to make such life style changes. Asking a person who commutes 20 miles to work or study to simply cycle is not a fair request, mainly due to the time and physical effort required to do so, but also the risk of injury by other less concerned commuters who are driving to work. This sort of solution only mitigates the problem… it must be solved from the root; the 20 mile fossil fuel burning commute.

Study shows that the happiness of a person is inversely proportional to the length of their commute Robert Putman; author of 'Bowling Alone' suggested the triangle of happiness.

The triangle of happiness represents the three sides to a professional; where they sleep, where they work and where they shop. The smaller the distances between these points the happier the person is… a long commute is proportional to an unhappy commuter. Reducing or merging the sides of the triangle can lead to happiness, eliminating the commute to work by working at home is a very good idea, however reducing the triangle to a single vertex would not be recommended as there would be no social interaction to be had and thus no happiness.

There has been much speculation as to the ideal dimension of the sides of the triangle of happiness; although this is still being debated it has been found, that in most cases the ideal size is 1.08450505250 miles* which by a staggering coincidence is the telephone number for the Citizens Advice Bureau in London.

Defaulting society out of standby

Standby functions on products improve the perceived performance with quick state changes from apparent 'Off' to 'On', this sort of function encourages wasteful behaviour as the product still consumes electricity on standby. Designers have the power to influence how a product is used, and steer the behaviour of the user towards a more sustainable operation. The standby function could be removed from the device and setting up a default auto-shutdown when the product is not in use.

"Much recent design has satisfied only evanescent wants and desires, while the genuine needs of man have often been neglected..." Extract from 'The Green Imperative', by Victor Papanek.

These approaches to sustainable design target the needs of the user as a member of our global civilization and the environment to lead a more sustainable life while still enjoying the comforts of technology. However not until the basic needs of humanity are fulfilled will everyone be ready to change the behavioural patterns of junkie consumerism that have marked our way of life for centuries.

Designers have generated throughout the decades desirability through different styles and gestures. We see concepts of flowing forms and graphical balance as desirable attributes. Now it is time to see fair-trade, low embodied energy and recyclability as desirable features, as much as we admire the purity of form, robustness or lightness in contemporary design.

Desirability by design could be a very efficient tool in bringing sustainable designed features to the general public. By swinging the demand from vane aesthetics to a more complete concept of beauty that embraces good design and sustainability, we could make sustainability truly sustainable.

A full version of this essay is available at: www.madeinbrunel.com

---

* Not based on fact; based on the distance walked in 5 minutes on a typical English village, the telephone number is correct (just remove the 1.).

Eco Bags Don't Grow on Trees

Anna West

Plastic bags have riddled the country since the 1970s. They are light and tough, and are carried by the wind to all areas of the environment. Once caught in trees or fences they last for over 500 years until they photodegrade getting into the waterways and often ending up in the food chain according to USGS.

Modbury, in South Devon, was the first town in the UK to completely ban plastic bags. Rebecca Hosking started the initiative in May 2007. She says in her book 'Ban the Plastic Bag', that the disposable plastic bag is only "a symbol for our unsustainable lifestyles". Modbury's actions brought the environmental implications of plastic bags to the attention of the media and kick-started other towns to start campaigns.

Consumers have become much more savvy about environmental issues and now demand retailers be more environmentally friendly. Many large retailers are doing something to reduce the use of plastic bags, either with an outright ban or by making a small charge. Some people have concerns about these efforts and point out, on the Daily Mail website for instance, that, "the turtle will still die regardless of whether the plastic bag cost 5p or not." We need to change our attitude to plastic bags and stop assuming it is our right to get one every time we go shopping.

Reusable bags are now widely available in the UK. They are sold in most major supermarkets and high street shops. Anya Hindmarch released the iconic I'm Not A Plastic Bag eco tote bag in July 2007. No other reusable bag has had such a vogue but it received some harsh criticism for the materials and manufacturing it used. The objective of the bag, to raise the profile of the plastic bag issue, is widely considered to have been achieved.

Reusable bags come in many shapes, sizes and materials. The best materials to choose are organic, natural materials. However, as the Modbury website details, it is important to consider the amount of energy it takes to make the bags, where the material is grown and how it is processed. The website also offers some questions that you can ask when you are looking to buy the ultimate reusable bag:

- Where has it come from? Avoid products from China which doesn't have a recognised organisation to govern organic or fair-trade products.
- Is it a fair-trade product? Look for a Fairtrade logo.
- Is the material bleached? Bleaching uses vast quantities of water and chemicals which can pollute the environment.
- Is the material organic? Look for the Soil Association logo.
- Have the materials been recycled? Look for materials that can be recycled when you've finished using the bag.
- Does it contain water or vegetable based inks or dyes? These are easier to treat at the recycling stage.
- If it comes from abroad, how has it reached you? Air freight instantly increases the carbon footprint of products.
- Are all of the materials natural? Waterproof linings can make recycling impossible.
- How much does it cost? A cheap bag is likely to have had corners cut somewhere in its production.

The most common materials used in commercially produced bags are cotton, jute and hemp. Fabrics can also be made from plant fibres like straw, maize, palm or bamboo. Alternatively, try a wicker basket. Not only are these materials sustainably grown but they are made locally using traditional craft techniques.

One particular type of reusable bag that appears to be environmentally friendly are the hard wearing plastic 'bags for life' which are available in most major supermarkets. They do not last for life and one sharp packet corner can cause a rip. Hoskins points out that they contain approximately 10 times more plastic than the standard bag which means they'll take longer to break down.

A big problem with the acceptance of reusable bags is the lack of information available to the public. If people were more aware of the environmental damage caused by plastic bags they would be more likely to take action against it. However, there are many people who wish to reduce their use of plastic bags and carry reusable bags with them.

One of the hottest topics in this debate is the use of biodegradable plastic. The best biodegradable plastic is starch based which means that it can be composted. Starch based products, from rice and potatoes, are organic and break down into carbon dioxide, water and mineral salts which is detailed by Rosewood Packaging.

Hopefully the increase in popularity and the steady change of attitude will help to improve the status of reusable bags. We need to find a way of making them appeal to as many people as possible and remind ourselves that 'free' plastic bags have only been available for the last 30 years. Everyone should carry a shopping bag, as many have done for years. It's not a large change of lifestyle but it makes all the difference.

Reducing the use of plastic bags isn't going to solve all of the environmental problems. We also need to reduce all the other plastic packaging we use. Removing plastic bags is the start. One step at a time will give us a much better chance of succeeding.

Plastic Bag Facts from 'Ban the Plastic Bag'

- Plastic bag litter kills at least 100,000 birds, whales, dolphins, seals, sea lions and turtles every year.
- Every person in the UK uses an average of 300 plastic bags every year which means that we use about one million bags every minute!
- We only use plastic bags for about 12 to 20 minutes before throwing them away.

So what you can do?

- Turn down the offer of a plastic bag when you're shopping.
- Always carry a reusable bag when you go out and put one or two in the back of your car.
- If you do forget and have to use a plastic bag, keep it and use it again, then take it to a supermarket and recycle it!

A full version of this essay is available at: www.madeinbrunel.com

4dimensional

Digital, online and multimedia based concepts.

In the last ten years, multimedia and internet technologies have become an essential part of everyday life. This digital era has altered our social behaviour, but is still relatively unexplored, giving rise to new design opportunities. Rapid interaction and communication is defined by speed, making our lives and the concepts within this chapter driven by the fourth-dimension - time.

thinking

Future Concepts for ABSOLUT

ABSOLUT product concepts, capturing the brand's core essence, have been created for the year 2020 to promote personal growth through social interaction.

The range offers an alternative to alcohol in a future society where its dangers and risks are known and understood by everyone.

Each product encompasses the discrete use of technology within inspiring forms, enhancing a stage of friendship through creation, strengthening and revival, in an overall effort to enhance social experiences.

Lucy Bradshaw
Industrial Design BSc

ABSOLUT InTouch
Future concept for ABSOLUT

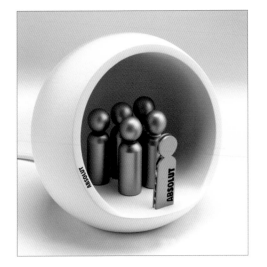

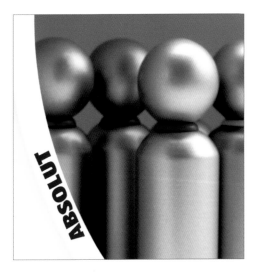

This concept for ABSOLUT is based on making connections with new people and keeping in touch with the people you care about.

The pocket-sized device holds your profile, which is transferred when two devices touch. This process humanises the exchange of personal details.

When not in use, it is stored at home in a physical address book with personalised figures symbolising different friendship groups. Each friend's details are uploaded to a different figure depending upon the group in which they belong. This creates a physical reminder of your friends always being there for you.

Mark Haite

Industrial Design & Technology BA

ABSOLUT Sport

Future concept for ABSOLUT

The device is designed to enhance the social aspects of an active friendship group whether skiing, snowboarding, jogging or cycling.

There are two main parts to the device; the first is the virtual retinal display, which projects an image straight onto the eye. The user then sees the position of different members of the group and journey statistics projected in front of them as a 3D image.

The second part of the device is a communication unit allowing different members of the group to communicate with each other whilst moving. The overall aim of the device is to enhance friendships by using technology to encourage group interaction.

Damon Murray-Morrish
Industrial Design & Technology BA

ABSOLUT Adornment
Future concept for ABSOLUT

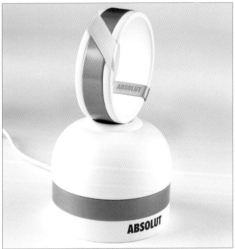

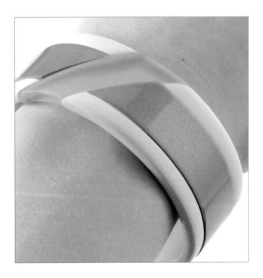

This product is designed for meeting new people and helping to strike up a conversation when it may not be obvious that you have something in common to talk about. The product works by the user uploading their profile onto the device, allowing them to reveal information about themselves that they are happy to disclose.

The device then scans for other devices in the immediate area that have similar profiles. An indication is then made to the wearers through small vibrations, pulsing light and the release of your favourite scent. Once the match is identified then an approach can be made and a conversation started.

Chloe Underhill
Industrial Design BSc

ABSOLUT Re-memory
Future concept for ABSOLUT

Future consumers will understand the damaging effects of alcohol; therefore the aim of Re-memory is to provide an alternative to alcohol to aid in the creation and extension of friendships.

Re-memory is a memory capture and recreation system. Friends wear wireless personal devices which capture their most stimulating moments, selected based on the user's heart rate.

At home the devices are stored in a memory pod, which recreates memories through video, audio and smell. As additional friends add their devices to the pod, their memories are added to the recreation.

Alex Weldon
Industrial Design BSc

ABSOLUT Skulptör
Future concept for ABSOLUT

The base unit displays a 3D holographic projection which reacts to different hand gestures. This enables a group of friends gathered around the device to sculpt virtually. The act of co-creation in this format produces light objects that can be saved and displayed at a later date to invoke happy memories for all individuals involved.

The unit is intended be used as an after dinner activity which, when not in use, can scroll through past creations, or display other holographic imagery.

Future Concepts for Penguin Books

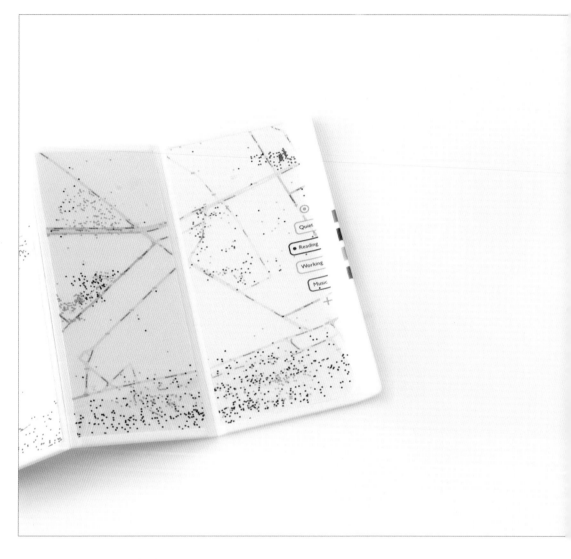

In 2023 it is projected that Penguin will have expanded upon their traditional roots as a publisher of books into the 'publishing' of products.

In a fast-paced, highly technological world Penguin Products add a human element to daily life. The psychological and emotional wellbeing of the user is the primary focus of their function.

Collectively, Penguin Products aim to provoke thought and imagination, provide a portal to another world and be a form of company. These are all qualities associated with the experience of reading that form the core of the Penguin brand.

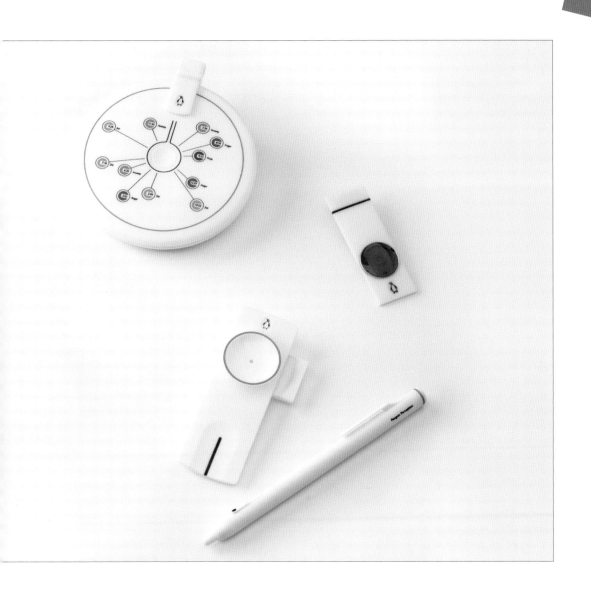

Dominic Burton
Industrial Design BSc

Penguin Perspective - The Other Map by D. Burton
Future concept for Penguin

Penguin Perspective allows people to understand their environment through the people that are inhabiting it. It does this by letting individuals broadcast their location and additional information, either about themselves, what they are doing or their immediate surroundings. This information is represented by a coloured dot on the map. The individual dots mean little by themselves but together they combine to convey a story to the user.

Alex Bygrave
Industrial Design BSc

Penguin Perception - A New World by A. Bygrave
Future concept for Penguin

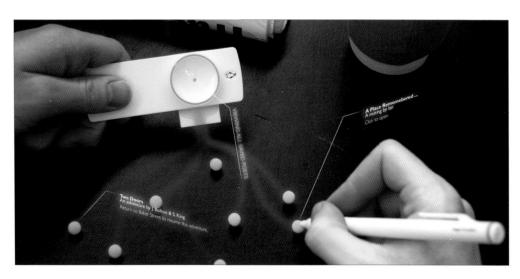

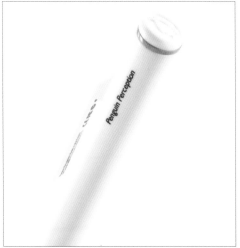

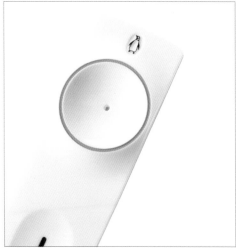

Society in 2023 is no longer disposable. Advances in technology are used to encourage human interaction rather than hinder it.

Penguin Perception allows users to interact virtually with reality. Individuals can read and publish virtual posts on real objects. Posts may contain anything from thoughts to drawings or photos. Alternatively they may be entire stories or adventures based around the location in which they are posted.

Penguin Perception is designed to increase in sentimental value with age. It is at the forefront of publishing, encouraging mental well-being through social interaction, expression and adventure.

Tim Holley
Industrial Design BSc

Penguin Journal - A Reflection of Self by T. Holley
Future concept for Penguin

The world in 2023 is fast-paced and highly technology driven, leaving little time for people to reflect upon day-to-day events. Well-being is a topic of great importance, with an increasing number of people turning to more proactive and introspective methods of caring for themselves.

The Penguin Journal allows the individual to 'write' their own story. It takes cues from the body, capturing only events that are meaningful to the user. By recording frequently overlooked events the Journal provokes thought and reflection - a key essence of the Penguin brand.

Neil Willetts
Industrial Design BSc

Penguin Teller - A Source of Knowledge by N. Willetts
Future concept for Penguin

In 2023 Penguin Books will have a Penguin Products imprint, producing a range of staple products from in house designers, and 'publishing' new ones from up and coming young designers.

The Penguin Teller encourages human interaction with others, by sharing knowledge relating to your personal media profile: literary, musical, cultural and historical.

The Teller keeps track of events visited, books read and music listened to, in order to allow others to develop an understanding of what it is you might like.

Through an emotional attachment to products, and developments in technology, the current norm of replacing a product when it is out of date will no longer apply.

Bokx TV
Online TV system

Bokx TV is an online television system that allows companies to create channels, upload content and specify when it will be broadcast through the use of virtual TV guides.

The fully integrated advertising system can then be used to sync promotional material with the video to maintain relevance; for example, product placement - when an actress sips from a can of Coca Cola in the video, the surrounding banner advertising can be changed to Coca Cola adverts.

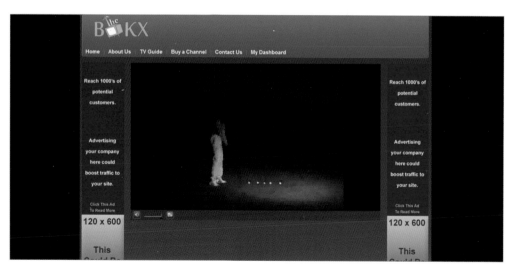

Lottie Booth
Multimedia Technology & Design BSc

Uniwise
Student website with integrated video content

Uniwise is a website designed to help students who have just received their A-Level results, so they can explore their options with regards to University.

To make the content more engaging for the viewer, Uniwise uses a presenter to communicate the main points, making Uniwise easier to relate to.

In conjunction with this, the website includes a series of videos covering a range of topics, featuring students talking about their experiences of University.

Members of the site are able to comment on, and discuss these videos, giving them a much-needed outlet for their fears and worries about University.

 UniWise

Search [   ]

Home | Starting University? | Not got the grades? | Contact Us

Didn't get the grades?
Don't Panic!

Accommodation

Student Life

Finance

Studying & Workload

Freshers Week

Time Management | Exams & Revision | Study Skills | Employability

Employability

With so many people coming out with a degree these days its important to give yourself the edge when it comes to employability. This may include:

Taking on extra responsibility at University like becoming a Course Rep.

Joining societies related to your course to show your enthusiasm for the subject.

Don't just rely on what you're taught in lectures, making sure you do lots of background research.

Get involved with a variety of extra-curricular activities to improve your skills in other areas.

You might consider doing a work placement year if your course allows it, to give you some valuable work experience.

Talk to people and ask lots of questions, University is a good chance to network and make contacts which can be very useful when you start working.

Student Videos

Contact Us | Sitemap | Terms of Use | Privacy Statement   UniWise

Dan Buckland
Multimedia Technology & Design BSc

The Dali Project
Dali's video

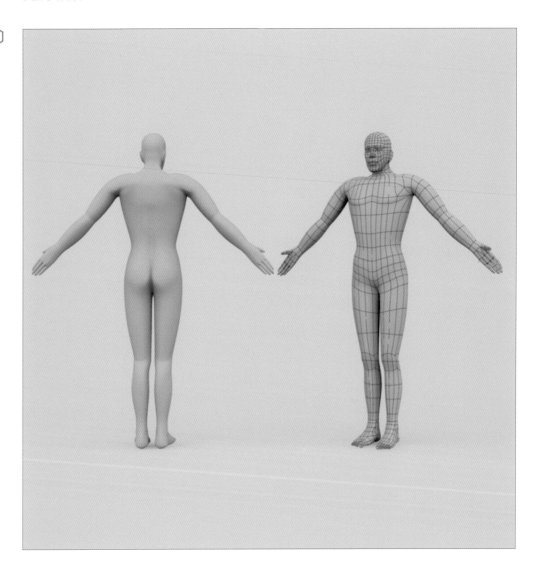

The Dali Project, is a re-imagining of surrealist painter Salvador Dali's most famous works, It brings life to a chosen selection of Dali's paintings through 3D visualisation and animation. The aim is to enhance Dali's original, surrealist visions rather than alter the meanings of the paintings themselves. 'Dali's Video' is the finished artefact, a minute long video showing Dali's creations in motion.

The video was created to look like Dali himself may have filmed it with the limited recording equipment available during the early years of his work.

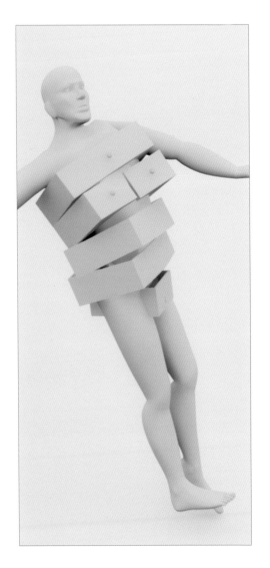

Jency Chong

Multimedia Technology & Design BSc

My Heart Needs

A young people heart guide on their health, confidence and kindness

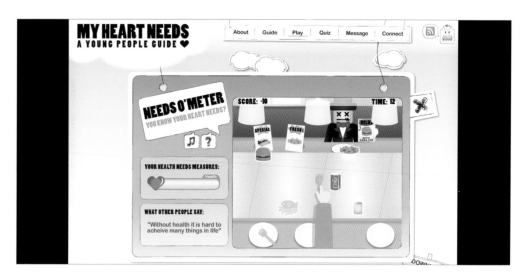

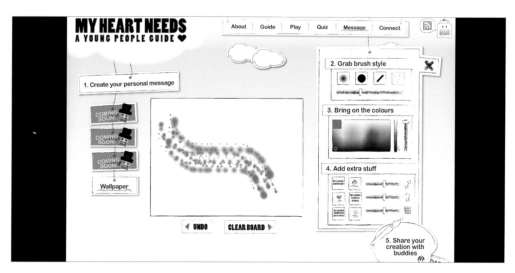

The aim of the project is to communicate three values: Health, Self-Confidence and Support to young people aged 15-22 years old. These values are essential; during this growth period they will start to develop their own thinking, taking responsibility, interacting with others and society.

This interactive microsite consists of features like a mini game, where the user needs to be aware of three status bars, Health, Confidence and Kindness. Personal messages can also be designed and shared. The site provides a fun and engaging environment that allows communication of these values.

Chris Dunne
Multimedia Technology & Design BSc

Dream Sequence from 'The Road'
3d animation

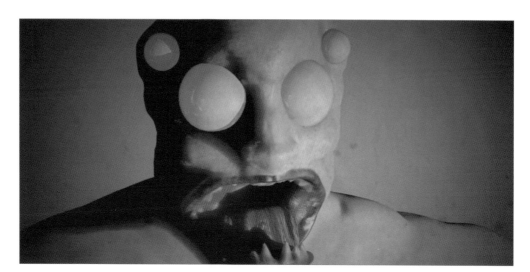

The aim of the project was to create a high quality 3D animation based on the book The Road by Cormac McCarthy (2006) that is both thought provoking and unsettling.

The majority of existing short 3D animations aim to be funny. However as 3D rendering technology improves there are ever increasing possibilities for innovative animation.

Using a combination of well established 3D methods and cutting edge techniques (including normal and ambient occlusion mapping) a highly detailed 3D animation has been produced.

Dom Fisher
Multimedia Technology & Design BSc

Misplaced Loyalty
Crime/thriller film targeting social/moral issues. Incorporating special fx

Misplaced Loyalty is a short fictional crime/thriller film reflecting upon real social problems like organised crime and moral issues, including greed and betrayal.

The film incorporates digital special effects features such as a car explosion, creating a genuine theatrical feel.

The story follows two friends who stand up against the head of a criminal gang that currently has control over a city. It also follows the life of a respected businessman and as the film progresses we find out more about his dark background and connections with the gang.

Tom Gentry
Broadcast Media Design & Technology BSc

Sure Thing, SPUD!
Visual teaching artefact for the learning disabled

Children with learning difficulties constitute a significant portion of pupils in primary and secondary education, and as such they can often feel condescended to and uncomfortable when presented with educational tools which are not well matched to their abilities.

Sure Thing, SPUD! is a video-based teaching aid which combats this by being tailored to audience's learning abilities and tastes.

It increases the effectiveness of lessons by employing a writing style suited to the audience's abilities as well as visual styles that effectively engage their minds to learning.

Sanaz Imanzadeh

Multimedia Technology & Design BSc

Crystal Clear

2d animation for a crystal meth awareness campaign

The aim of this project was to create an awareness campagin around the increasing use of Methamphetamines.

The latest data from America suggests that 50% of national HIV cases result from Methamphetamine use. Expansion into Britain has become apparent, with Methamphetamines being popular with 10% of London's gay community.

As shown in the animation, recreational use can quickly turn to dependency. The story, which is based on true events, features 'Frank', who gradually destroys his life as we follow the suffering he feels using colour to illustrate the environment and society.
The story ends with events forcing 'Frank' to seek professional help.

"It really has happened. Gradually, almost without anyone noticing: The internet has become mainstream. YouTube is an old man and Google has become the all seeing eye. The world is now truly digital. That's why now more than ever before Interactive Thinking is required to come up with big ideas the right kind of big ideas that connect with people in this digital world.

Those are simple ideas, brave ideas. Ideas that can be advertised as opposed to advertising ideas. Ideas that become pop culture. They can be useful tools or entertaining content. Ideas that put the user in charge and turn him into a participant. It's not easy, but when you get it right and your idea flies, it's the most amazing thing. Damn you internet - I love you."

Flo Heiss

Clare Lee
Multimedia Technology & Design BSc

Project Nimis
Human fat to power the world

Project Nimis takes a lighthearted look at a solution to the impending energy crisis thus far not discussed: using human fat to power the world.

This animation imagines a future where humanity's impact has left other forms of energy production unfeasible and man must finally bear the cost of its excesses.

Its aim is to increase perception of personal responsibility for environmental issues in an engaging manner, without resorting to platitudes and moralising.

Saghar Masihi
Multimedia Technology & Design BSc

Road Safety Awareness
An interactive game for children

An average of 37 children under 16 were killed or seriously injured every week on roads in the UK in 2007. Currently most children under nine do not have a true sense of speed and distance. Road safety awareness skills might therefore be learnt in early ages more effectively through the use of interactive learning tools.

An educational interactive flash game was developed for use by young children to practice road safety basics. The children can interact with the game to move within the simulated roads using a Wii remote control or a keyboard.

Besides helping them to learn basic skills the product can also boost confidence while the child is playing in the virtual world without being accompanied by an adult.

Paul O'Hara
Multimedia Technology & Design BSc

Hot Pursuit
Anti-drink drive campaign

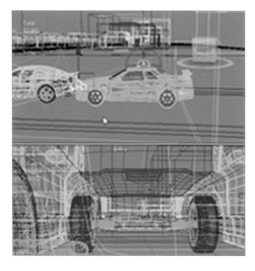

Every year 500 people are killed on British roads as a direct consequence of drink driving, with the main offenders being young male drivers. Hot Pursuit is a 3D-based project aimed at communicating the anti drink drive message to the audience in a new and invigorating manner.

The animation consists of a short car chase set within an urban environment, which chronicles the demise of a drink driver, and in the process incorporates various elements of traditional cinematography.

Various post-production techniques were applied to the artifact, in order to achieve the desired visual styling for the piece, which will be distributed via the Web.

Sarah Turner

Product Design Engineering BSc

amBX for Console

Console lights for amBX, the next level in computer gaming

amBX entered the gaming market two years ago with enhanced experiences for PC gamers. The technology uses lights situated around the PC screen, which mimic the on-screen content. They are now planning to expand into the lucrative console market, where the combined sales of the Wii, Playstation 3 and Xbox 360 have reached an estimated 61 million units worldwide.

The project aims to design lights for console use. Many complex issues have been addressed including TV sizes, the product's new environment and designing for the different console styles.

The final product will be demonstrated working with a TV and console.

How is the Role of the Designer Changing?

Dominic Burton

It is estimated that the design phase of a new product determines over 80% of the environmental impact the product will have according to the European Commission. Much is now understood about how to change the environment, however products will always have some sort of impact. No impact would imply no product. Should designers ask the question 'should this product be designed' more often?

It is suggested by the authors of the book 'Cradle to Cradle' that a more sensible way of controlling the environmental impact of products is to change their nature from being something that is owned to being a service. For example, instead of buying a television set, you pay for so many hours of use. This is not a completely new idea, people currently rent televisions, however this is not supported by businesses and therefore not made appealing.

As can be seen from the recent global economic crisis, ordinary people will make judgments about an industry or profession when things go wrong. If a critical point was reached in the ecological health of the planet would citizens accept that collectively the people with the knowledge and power to act made the best effort possible? Designers clearly have much to think about.

When making his Nobel Prize acceptance speech, Harold Pinter, the late playwright, referred to a writing of his from 1958: "There are no hard distinctions between what is real and what is unreal, nor between what is true and what is false. A thing is not necessarily either true or false; it can be both true and false. I believe that these assertions still make sense and do still apply to the exploration of reality through art. So as a writer I stand by them but as a citizen I cannot. As a citizen I must ask: What is true? What is false?"

Pinter went on to refer to matters of arguably much more immediate moral questionability than the slow degradation of the earth's ecological systems. However the way it addresses one's consciousness of the difference between ethics in one's profession and as an individual articulates some of the reflection and re-evaluation that may be required and even underway in some professions holding the power to change the future.

Victor Margolin sees designers as occupying a 'dialectical space between the world that is and the world that could be,' and therefore sees them as potentially holding a powerful position. However he notes that, compared with other groups of people, designers have made few calls for social change. Similarly Nicola Morelli comments that designers have traditionally 'interpreted their social role as complementary to business strategies'. However now as changes in our understanding of the extent to which industrial activity impacts nature this role is changing.

If the role of the designer adapts according to changes in the world it is therefore useful to look at viewpoints on how the current world view was established. In his book, 'The Turning Point,' Fritjof Capra holds up Descartes' view of nature as a machine, that can be understood by breaking it down into small pieces, as the current mode of thinking that has failed to take account of the ecological systems of the world.

The dominant shift of perspective proposed in order to help rectify ecological imbalances is based around these principles of having a more coherent 'systems thinking' view of the world. For instance the United Nations Environment Programme (UNEP) promotes both life-cycle thinking and product service systems. The higher agenda of sustainability and design in international governing bodies provides motivation for change from non-business contexts to new contexts of inception.

In trying to understand the failures of modern town planning Victor Papanek looks to the past, suggesting modern planners do not understand the 'basic purpose of living' as form givers of the past did. People often prefer to inhabit old quarters of cities built hundreds of years ago, than the new areas supposedly built for them. Papanek cites Aristotle as expressing this purpose lost in modern planning, 'men form communities not for justice, peace, defense, or traffic, but for the sake of the good life. This good life has always meant the satisfaction of four basic social desires: conviviality, religiosity, intellectual growth, and politics.' We can therefore say that something should not be designed just because it is sustainable. The role of the designer, it appears then should also bear reference to these notions of designing to cater to people's fundamental desires.

It is difficult to know if, or when, environmental and ethical responsibility will become the norm in design. Writing in the Ecologist, Nick Kettles comments on the designing of mobile phones as fashion items suggesting this has created the culture of replacing them every 18 months, consequently creating a society where happiness is measured by how recently you have replaced your mobile phone.

However, should not consumers have the freedom to consume whatever they wish? It could be argued that they are not the ones deciding considering the amount of advertising and aggressive marketing of mobile phone retailers. In fact, according to the UNEP "It is becoming more and more evident that consumers are increasingly interested in the 'world that lies behind' the product they buy. This increasing awareness about environmental and social issues is a sign of hope. Governments and industry must build on that."

The economic context out of which a product is born clearly determines to some extent its ethical and environmental qualities. Understanding these qualities is an extremely complex process, making it difficult to rely on the judgment of consumers. Change therefore needs to come from all directions not just from designers, consumers, business or politicians. Designers have long been seen as agents capable of bringing together many disciplines and aims; this seems the role they must continue to play but maybe to a different song.

A full version of this essay is available at: www.madeinbrunel.com

Crisis; the Creative Catalyst

James Vardy

Crisis is an increasingly used term in today's economic and environmental climate. It is a word associated with extreme negative 'tests' of our human abilities as a species.

Today's crises may seem unrecoverable, but we have come through worse situations and gained much knowledge from the experience. Wherever a crisis occurs there is a creative success story resulting from adversity. Why do so many creative developments occur when everything appears to be against us and creative prosperity seems significantly more difficult? Crisis creativity is a reoccurring pattern and a fundamental human characteristic.

The most catastrophic recurring man-made crisis is war. Wars have historically been times of rapid innovation. The very first chemotherapy drug was developed from mustard gas, which ironically was the first weapon of mass destruction. Blood transfusions became a reality as the demand increased and camaraderie between soldiers meant there were sufficient donors.

These breakthroughs have shaped the world today. Some had no other reasoning behind them other than the pressure of the situation and the need to be creative as existing solutions were not sufficient.

What other reasons explain why creative ideas not only come about, but potentially flourish, in times of crisis? Looking at past crises, patterns and characteristics can be identified and incorporated into our own creative processes as a catalyst for change. Boden explains in her book 'The Creative Mind' that the greatest factor affecting crisis creativity is that creativity and risk are intrinsically linked, since by definition anything creative involves a move into the unknown. During day-to-day life risk is low and therefore a truly creative act can be interpreted as an unnecessary risk. Today's corporate world breeds this outlook as responsibilities with regards to stakeholders outweigh the need for progression. The risks were not just financial, but also of feeling humiliated if an idea fails or stupid for mentioning a poorly thought out concept. In a crisis situation however risk is already high and therefore a new approach may seem less dangerous than it previously would.

Crisis puts constraints on the creative development process inspiring change and this is especially true of the environmental crises. With projected models of water levels and climate temperature becoming more familiar it becomes easier to relate to the situation and creative solutions are emerging at a faster pace.

Evidence in fossil records show that there have also been times of rapid and significant change within short periods of time (Lewin, 'Human Evolution'. 2004) in our own evolution. Competition is not enough to account for such anomalies; these sudden changes in fossil records coincide with dramatic environmental crises. Without this creative aspect of evolution species would not adapt and would most likely perish.

Just as we see the mechanism of evolution contributing to survival and development over millions of years in nature, in the short term we can also see a similar mechanism of adaptation in our own innovative progression as a response to crisis.

Early stone tools dating back to 100,000 BC show evidence of clothing production. It comes as no surprise that the dates of these tools match with a crisis: the Ice Age (Stringer, C). Such an obvious link allows us to theorise that the early production of clothes was a creative response to a crisis. Similarly we can start to consider that early hunting tools may have been developed to tackle larger animals in times of food crisis or as a way of tackling a predatory threat.

In nature there is no change without competition or crisis and without either development may slow or even stop. This phenomenon can be seen in cockroaches that have not evolved for 350 million years as a result. This suggests, as we become more technologically suited to our environment progress will slow.

Crises Today

The 'credit crunch' is today's economic crisis, but is it driving any creative change? Yes, the best way to strengthen the economy is through innovation and growth, this mechanism a motivation factor rather than opportunity, although governments in time are likely to offer incentives to inspire creative business growth.

Canon is a company not known for radical change and although they invest heavily in research and development they rarely make radical leaps. Their attitude towards the financial crisis of "going into hibernation" can be linked back to the earlier discussed theories in that Canon has a relatively low risk, because they operate in so many markets and as a result spread their risk amongst these differing sectors. Without the need for radical creativity there is no drive or signs of it.

Quite the opposite of this reaction can be seen from The Guardian. Ex-Financial and Economics Editor and now Technology Columnist Victor Keegan sees real opportunity for the news firm in the crisis. His view is that people will have less expendable income and, as unemployment rises dramatically web use will boom because of the prepaid nature of the service, he predicts huge growth of The Guardian online. Other technology experts agree on this potential change in consumer patterns with Google and other online giants expected to do extremely well form the current crisis. Perhaps the reason The Guardian have identified an area for creative growth is that they are vulnerable to change and risk in the coming years, particularly as we move towards a paperless society.

Why then does The Guardian see this opportunity and not Canon? Perhaps as mentioned before it is because Canon has a low risk due to its spread of markets whereas The Guardian has a relatively high risk exposure because it offers one main service: news, making them much more vulnerable. Because of the increased perceived crisis affecting The Guardian their clarity of task to seek new opportunities and make creative change is that much greater than that of Canon. It is quite plausible that we shall see The Guardian rise like a phoenix from the ashes of the economic crisis thanks to a high perceived risk level.

What we can take away is that creative adaptation in times of crisis and change is a very real innate human ability and is a response to survival in an unknown scenario, a trait we have inherited, developed and now apply today.

A full version of this essay is available at: www.madeinbrunel.com

Simon Fraser University, Canada

Adrian Bisek, Jin Fan, Justin Mah, Shannon Tinkley

Bike App

The best of both worlds – Get in. Work out

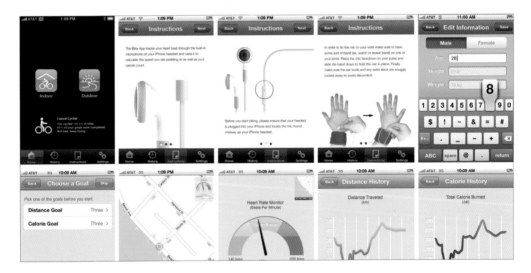

When it comes to exercise many activities take place both indoors and outdoors, especially when it involves cycling, making it difficult to track one's overall progress. Whether it's hitting the trails on a sunny day or hopping on a bike at the gym for some cardio, Bike App caters to its user's needs and enhances cycling routines of all levels. Using iPhone's built-in microphone and GPS capabilities,

Bike App processes data like calories burned and heart rate into visually motivational and informative displays. Challenge yourself by creating goals, tracking your history, and breaking record times. Bike App makes working out fun!

It monitors your cardiovascular output using the microphone in the headset. With indoor and outdoor settings, a user can easily track their workouts and challenge their previous results. The Bike App is designed to generate an enjoyable and rewarding experience for users of all athletic levels. Aside from helping to set goals and track progress, the application is designed to create self-competition in a motivational and entertaining manner.

In addition to the video and map screens, there are visualization screens that display information like total calories, time, and kilometers traveled to document overall use. All of the Bike App features were iteratively developed and extensively tested throughout the entire development.

Simon Fraser University, Canada
Evangeline Chan, Raymond Chan, Kenneth Ho, Bill Ng, Siena Tsang, Karon Wong

Glowbal
Interactive Window allowing consumers to be emotionally and physically connected

The development of Glowbal was targeted towards one main goal; to promote HSBC Bank Canada and its offerings to prospective clients with intrinsic worth information through an interactive window display that holds the captivating elements to attract potential clients. This display transforms dull, unappealing windows into vast, motion-activated interactive window displays that take hold of the attention of participants passing by it. Glowbal is a high impact interactive window display that contains interactive images and animated clips as its main attraction component.

Living in the modern technological world, brochures and posters no longer attract potential consumers, especially for traditional banks such as HSBC. We hope to bring the young consumers an impressive experience and give them the opportunity to see banking in a different way through the

different kinds of interaction and engagement that this interactive window will bring upon them.

During Glowbal's development process, team Besrkk have researched motion-detection and gesture recognition. The base method that the team used for motion-detecting was image subtraction; a traditional way of tracking movements by comparing the difference between two images. To provide the participants with absolute control and the ability to navigate throughout the interface, the team utilized the background subtraction method, which compares the current image with a background image. Therefore, whatever is not initially in the background will be detected.

Simon Fraser University, Canada

Kyle Fox, Justin Holmes, Daniel Lee, Michael Malyuk

HIVE

Bee Line into Connection: Social Networking that Contextualises the Buzz

HIVE is about connecting individuals while on the go by creating a digital 'aura' that creates connections through interest, trend and radar functions. HIVE installs on an iPhone or iPod Touch, providing the user with a sixth sense while waiting at a bus-stop, having a coffee or even shopping. The radar links you to those with similar qualities so that you can create a buzz about your passions and interests, and encourage face-to-face or heart-to-heart conversation.

While current models of social networking lack dynamic creation of new connections between individuals, HIVE is positioned to redefine social networking as a service that goes beyond the previous confines of this genre. Our application departs from existing services by seeking to remove the intermediary, linking individuals to each other and their environment directly based on proximity and interests. By bringing this ability into the real world, HIVE makes

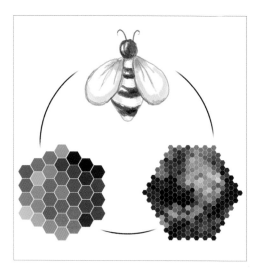

social networking an active possibility that facilitates making new connections versus reinforcing existing ones.

Choosing to base HIVE on a mobile platform opens up a world of newly afforded interactions. Whilst the entire mobile industry is making rapid leaps in technological achievements, there are two mobile devices that stand out from the crowd—the iPhone and iPod Touch. Apple's mobile lineup offers more than just hardware however, the iPhone and iPod Touch have an entire culture of their own and a devoted demographic that is not afraid to download and play with new applications. Furthermore, Apple's publicly available SDK makes developing for the devices efficient and convenient.

Simon Fraser University, Canada

Aleksandra Skibicki, Jenny Thai

K.I.T (Keep In Touch)

Use of tangible and online interactions to reconnect friendships through emotions.

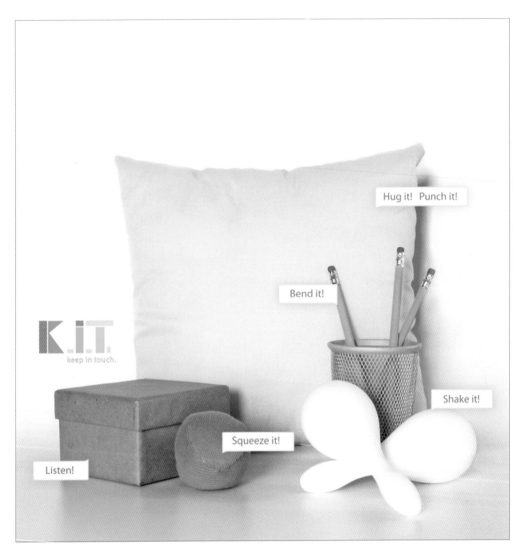

The use of online social networks such as Facebook and Twitter connect us with "everyone" yet at the same time leads to a loss of intimate connections between close friendships and other relationships. While the nature of these networks facilitate surface level communication, K.I.T enables deeper communication through the greater expression of emotions.

Our aim is to reconnect close relationships and provid better emotional health, support, and awareness. Emotion is important for everyday social interaction and brings value and life to communication.

K.I.T. comes as a package of interactive, tangible everyday objects that can be placed around the home. Each emotion is matched to an object that can be used to physically express the emotion and this gives people a natural, physical way to express, release and act on their emotions.

The expressed emotions are transferred to a private online network that is shared with close friends and family, with each user requiring a K.I.T. package to participate.

This enables online users to be aware of one another's emotional states, responding through written messages, voice messages and photos. Each user can also writeor record their own message to accompany their current emotional state. Emotional histories are also available to be viewed, providing an interesting perspective on emotions over a period of time.

Simon Fraser University, Canada

Jin Fan, Kyle Jung, David Chi Hang Ko, Justin Mah, Jessica Wai Yee Yu

The Looking Glass

Responsive fibre optics installation that explores the alternate self

The Looking Glass is an audiovisual immersive installation that explores the perception of alternate self. Users are immersed in a responsive and dynamic environment as they interact with the abstract silhouette projected on a glowing fibre optic wall.

The environment's state is continuously transformed by the user's gestures and auditory input. Any sound emitted by the users is echoed and causes the projection to change colours. The relationship unfolds as users engage in a dialog and examine how their movements shape the artificial extension. The connection between users' presence and environment's response drive the evolution of The Looking Glass.

The 2,700 threads of fibre optics that are attached to the frame create a texture that invites the users to touch, feel and communicate with their alternate self.

The Looking Glass explores the boundary between digital and physical experience by allowing visitors to touch the individually lit fibres – pixel-like elements of their abstract silhouette. It fosters an immersive and sensory experience by integrating tactile, visual and audio elements. As visitors move, talk and touch the installation, it manifests user's emotions and self-awareness.

Based on observations, users are fascinated by the dynamic color changes and abstractness of their silhouettes. Instead of presenting an accurate reflection of the users, the abstract projections offer users with more room for interpretation and reflection.

Simon Fraser University, Canada

On Ying Cheng, Kenneth Ho, Henry Lin, Denesa Yip

WEARME
One piece is all you need

To celebrate the Vancouver 2010 Winter Olympics, a product designed to improve people's experience at the event. WEARME is a multi-functional scarf that allows the user to wear it with their own style. The design was inspired by the elderly and their need to keeping warm. This product does not just provide warmth, it also "connects" people with its interactive element.

Participating in many winter activities requires people to be situated in cold temperature for an extended period of time. Proper winter gear is essential to protect the body from the bitter environment; however, it always becomes a hassle as it increases bulkiness and hinders movement

The neck, ears, and hands are the most exposed in cold weather, and people feel that these body parts are more sensitive to cold temperature, so we designed WEARME to serve the purpose of a scarf, hat, and mitts.

WEARME is made of flannel on one side to retain heat, and a water resistant fabric on the other to protect wearers from harsh weather. There are main pockets at the ends for users to place their hands, and within are small interior pouches to hold heating packs of various sizes. These packs provide a secondary heat source when needed.

A hood protects against rain or snow, and keeps the face and ears warm. The hood can be folded and stored in a hidden compartment within the scarf when not in use. The retractable feature also exists to accommodate jackets and coats that have their own hood.

humanistic

Products and concepts which improve the lives of specific target users.

Humanistic design and engineering thinking is at the heart of creating innovative opportunities to affect people's daily lives for the better on both a global, corporate and personal scale. Humanistic Thinking generates socially aware concepts, brands and strategies that are specifically developed to improve the lives of individuals, whatever their needs.

thinking

Future Concepts for Dulux

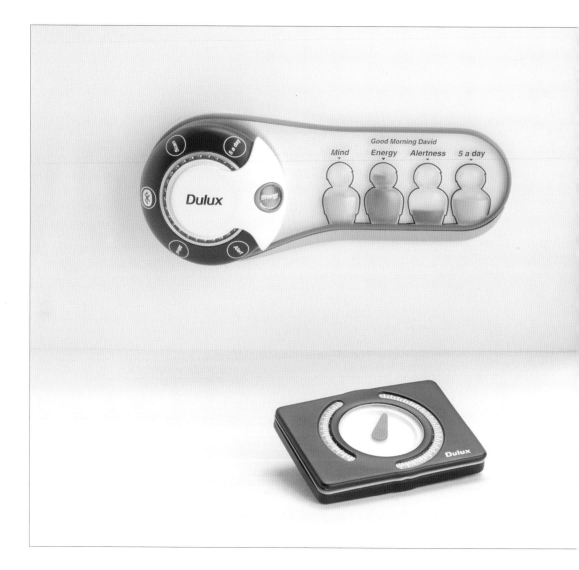

Dulux in 2025 has developed to match the needs of the Baby Boomer generation; those born between 1946 and 1964. Baby Boomers are outgoing, intelligent, pro-active and opinionated customers.

They will hold the greatest combined personal wealth in the UK and form the largest age band across the population.

The Dulux brand will retain its quality, trust and wit, and in 2025, Dulux will also be a brand of networking, self-actualisation, optimism, integrity, intelligence and youthful presence. Dulux is about life and making the most of it. The artefacts presen]ted here exemplify these values through health, home, exploration and relationships.

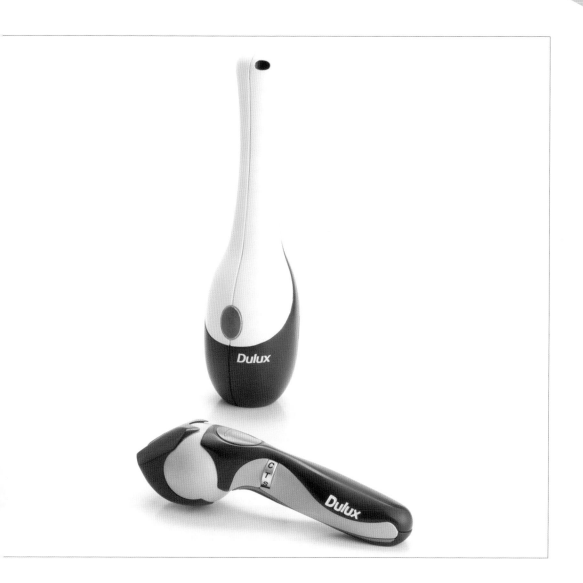

Oli Gould
Industrial Design BSc

Dulux Spot
Future concept for Dulux

This product expands on the home and family characteristics of the Dulux brand to encompass all social interaction by the year 2025. It targets the needs of the prosperous Baby Boomer generation.

In this modern age, and more so in 2025, much significance is placed on the digital locality of others compared to their corporeal locality. Baby Boomers, however, value physical interaction.

In a world of overriding digital content, this product increases awareness of the physical locations of friends and relatives by reacting to their proximity and assisting in their location in an engaging way.

Andrew Liddle
Industrial Design BSc

Dulux Savour
Future concept for Dulux

The Savour is a future concept for Dulux. It allows you to capture and recreate those memorable culinary delights from your travels exactly as you remember it. This intelligent cutlery, consisting of knife, fork and spoon, will analyse your food while you eat, identifying all the ingredients and quantities used.

This will then be wirelessly uploaded onto an Internet database and converted into a recipe, while also sourcing the ingredients in your hometown from a list of local suppliers. Now you can recreate and share those treasured moments with your closest family and friends back home.

Benjamin Scott
Industrial Design BSc

Dulux Pip
Future concept for Dulux

A step into the future. The Dulux Pip concept offers an opportunity to obtain ultimate flow and expression of self in any environment, allowing for different levels of customisable perception in a variety of downloadable applications. The product is designed to identify visual sources of excitement and stimulation, be it colour, shape or texture.

By doing so it will be able to suggest options for spacial layout within an environment indicative of a more expressive lifestyle.

The concept is designed to encourage user interaction, the more it interacts with a user the more it will learn about them.

Daniel Worboys
Industrial Design BSc

Dulux Balance
Future concept for Dulux

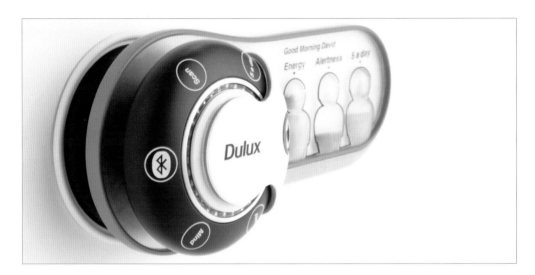

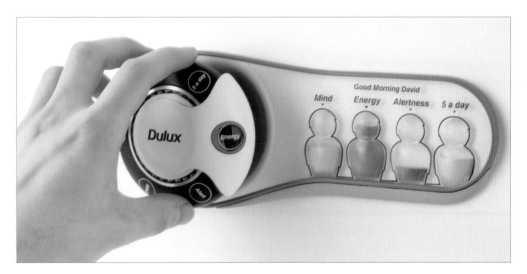

Baby Boomers now have the time to enjoy longer breakfasts, leisurely walks and more daily activities. However for some, their bodies are feeling slightly older than their minds so health has become an increasingly important aspect of their new routines.

Dulux Balance encompasses the brand values associated with Dulux, an honest, wholesome quality product aimed at improving general well-being.

Featuring fingertip blood monitoring technology behind a clean yet witty form. Dulux Balance enables suggestive guidance towards keeping a balanced diet enabling food tailoring within the user's calendar.

Dulux Balance creates opportunities for Baby Boomers to tailor their diet to make the most of the day's events, whilst learning about food groups and various health aspects.

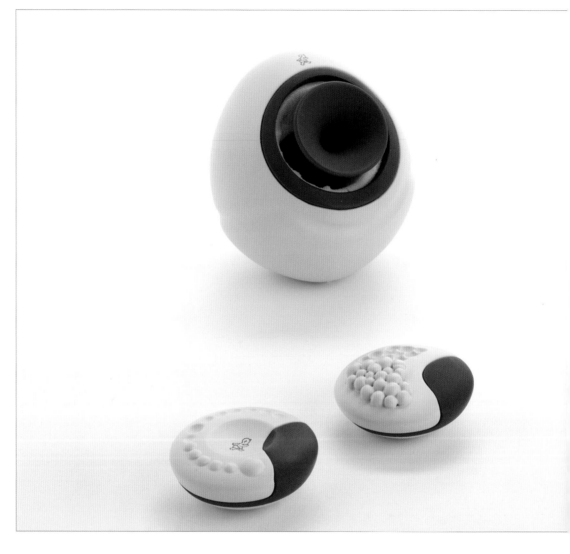

Iconically recognised throughout Britain as a maternally orientated brand, Fairy has been an integral part of domestic life within the UK for generations. These contextual products are individually focused on transcending this strong association of family values to more contemporary compelling issues.

These products address deeply emotive subjects including post partum blues, teenage pregnancy, fathers for justice and left out child syndrome to help 'Soften their world more than Ever'.

Lloyd Axten
Industrial Design & Technology BA

Fairy 'Keeper'
Future concept for Fairy

Fairy 'Keeper' is designed to decrease sibling rivalry between a first and newborn, promoting harmony in the home. The product is effectively two parts, the main 'Keeper' is a nightlight for the newborn child, and the 'Shmoo' is a small interactive device for the older child.

The product instills a sense of responsibility on the elder sibling by giving them the 'Shmoo' to look after. Through use of haptic interface the 'Shmoo' can be charged by being squeezed, rubbed and warmed. It is placed in the 'Keeper' at night to power a nightlight for the newborn child.

Jack Cheatle

Industrial Design & Technology BA

Fairy 'Godmother'

Future concept for Fairy

Teenage pregnancy affects over 43,000 girls in the United Kingdom. The Fairy 'Godmother' is a conceptual product that helps aid teenage mothers through the difficulties of pregnancy. It uses a worldwide wireless Internet connection to connect to independent databases.

When the teenage expectant asks the Fairy 'Godmother' a question, voice recognition technology is used to communicate with the information database, an answer is calibrated and sent back. The ultimate ambition is to see educated and informed decisions being made by the young individuals; harbored by technology, and supported by the knowledge and wisdom of thousands

Fairy 'Lift'
Future concept for Fairy

Fairy 'Lift' is a pocked-sized 'mirror' for women affected by Post-Partum Blues.

Designed to reach withdrawn women, the product attempts to trigger an emotional response through the distortion of one's own image. This tactfully allows the user to express their emotive reactions, be it through laughter or tears, to help them feel better and paradoxically regain a sense of self.

The 'mirror' will randomly generate a new distortion each time the product is closed, and captures the user's image through use of an embedded camera. The product also allows the storage of small keepsakes in the soft lining of its bottom half.

Courtney Wood
Industrial Design & Technology BA

Fairy 'Moment'
Future concept for Fairy

Looking into the future of the Fairy brand, Fairy 'Moment' uses bubbles to provide visual and tactile stimuli to count down the days until a parent and child are together. Pressing an 'I'm thinking of you' button sends a gentle pulse of warmth to the other device.

The child's piece uses bubbles in an unstructured manner to provide a soft representation of time. The parents uses a dial to provide visual indication of the days left. When parent and child meet again so do their Fairy 'Moments', with the child's piece sitting on top of the parent's to charge.

Future Concepts for Marlboro

The Marlboro brand is about freedom, exploration and masculinity. These qualities were merged with baby boomer personas who are independent, hardworking and forever young. This provided future concepts for Marlboro that aim to fulfill the idealistic aspirations of the male baby boomer generation by using Marlboro's values of quality and masculinity to provide a means of escape from their hectic modern lifestyles.

Marianne Kernohan
Industrial Design BSc

Marlboro Memento - Escape through memories
Future concept for Marlboro

Memento is mountain bike armour for the Baby Boomer generation. Ergonomically designed to protect the leg against rocks when they fall, this armour has a sacrificial aluminium plate that records each scratch and dent. When the plate is too damaged, a specially designed mechanism holding the plate in place can be released, allowing a new plate to be attached for that next trip down the mountain.

Memento allows the user to 'escape' back to their time on the track as well as giving them the opportunity to show to others that a few knocks and scrapes will not stop them.

Pui-Jun Lam
Industrial Design BSc

Marlboro Maven - Escape through anticipation
Future concept for Marlboro

Maven allows the user to scan information from a recently discovered bottle of wine, which can be wirelessly transferred to any electronic device and digitally stowed away ready to be proudly shown off to friends.

The anticipation of collecting another bottle and showing it off allows them to mentally 'escape' every time they looks through the collection while planning the next journey to acquire that desired bottle of wine.

Nital Patel
Industrial Design BSc

Marlboro Phono - Escape through sound
Future concept for Marlboro

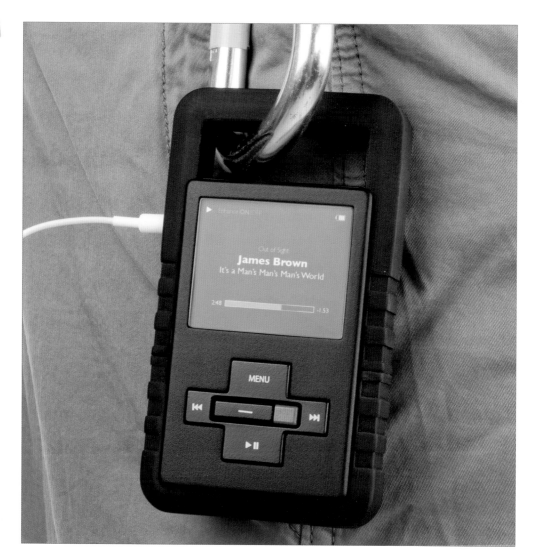

Marlboro in 2025, with a new target audience of the Baby Boomer generation, and a new direction with its product portfolio that offers the sense of 'escape'.

Human senses can be used to exude masculinity. The portable Marlboro Phono music player is one approach that enables the targeted users to 'escape', by listening to oozingly rich, high quality, music.

Phono has also been designed to automatically equalise and enhance audio output according to different outdoor surroundings, thus, eliminating the need for volume control all together. The 'ruggedized' look and feel makes a directly noticeable connection with the perceived values of the Marlboro brand as being rugged, masculine and reflective of the great outdoors.

Annika Pugh
Industrial Design & Technology BA

Marlboro Comrade - Escape through trust
Future concept for Marlboro

The Marlboro Comrade is a rescue knife that instils trust in its user. Every part of the knife has its purpose: it will make the male Baby Boomer marvel at its detail and feel like an alpha male when using it. It encompasses the Marlboro 'escape' brand through angularity and a streamlined aesthetic, but still affords a comfortable grip.

The knife can be held in many positions and be used for many different tasks, but is primarily used to aid rescue and will be most useful to its user in giving them a sense of preparation and safety on an outdoor adventure.

Kirsten M A Revell

Industrial Design BSc

Marlboro Explore - Escape through adventure
Future concept for Marlboro

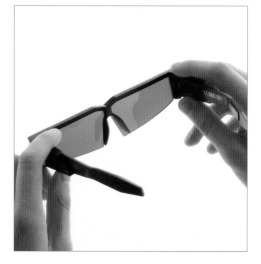

In 2025, overseas travel is a luxury and smoking is illegal. The Marlboro brand has extended its product range to realise the positive associations of its brand essence with non-tobacco related forms of 'escape', linking with Google Earth, the number one provider of 'virtual overseas holidays'.

Targeting the Baby Boomer generation, who are aware of the brand's masculine, rugged, outdoors attributes and its association with Formula 1 motor racing, a concept for video glasses has been developed. This provides instantaneous escape with the sensation of speed, freedom and beautiful horizons. Sound is transmitted by bone conduction and the latest iPod transmits video and audio data wirelessly, whilst also providing a mechanism for direction and acceleration control.

Future Concepts for Petits Filous

Taking on the World - is the new strap line for Petits Filous to highlight the new brand values of the company, empowering children's learning and development both physically and emotionally.

The concepts aim to promote adventure and outdoor physical activity, encouraging children to get close to nature and want to get stuck in to developing their imagination and learn through play and exploration leading to a healthier lifestyle.

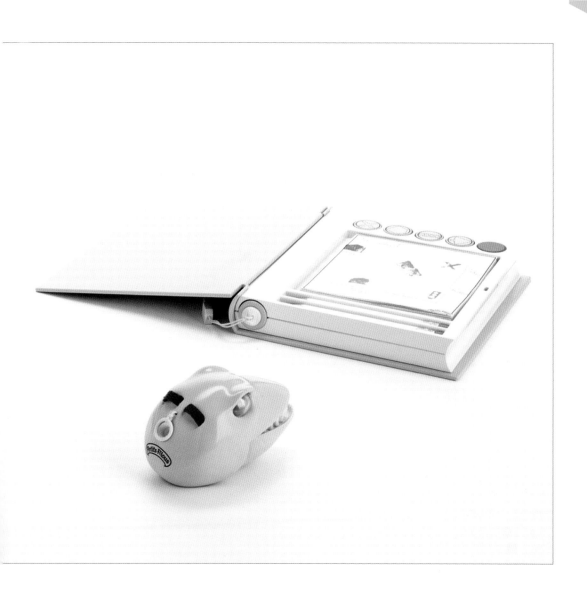

Filipe Almeida
Industrial Design & Technology BA

Petits Filous Galoshes
Future concept for Petits Filous

'Taking on the World' - the new strap line for Petits Filous is used to highlight the new brand values and empower children's learning and development both physically and emotionally.

Petits Filous Galoshes encourage adventure and outdoor physical activity, helping them stay safe every step they take.

Getting close to nature and wanting to get stuck in, Petits Filous Galoshes are ideal for developing a child's imagination by learning through play and exploration leading to a healthier lifestyle.

Robert Merriman
Industrial Design & Technology BA

Petits Filous Journey Journal
Future concept for Petits Filous

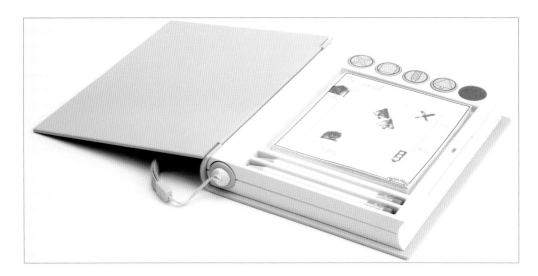

A product that is designed for the Petits Filous 'Taking on the World' product range, this product helps children in an urban environment to explore and learn about navigation and direction.

While the child is walking, they interact with the trigger to log where they have been, this trigger unlocks the book which prints a map of the journey they have just taken, the map can then be labelled with key landmarks from the journey which can challenge and develop the child's memory. These maps are stored in the book and can be used again by the child and parent.

Harley Smith
Industrial Design & Technology BA

Petits Filous Textures All Around
Future concept for Petits Filous

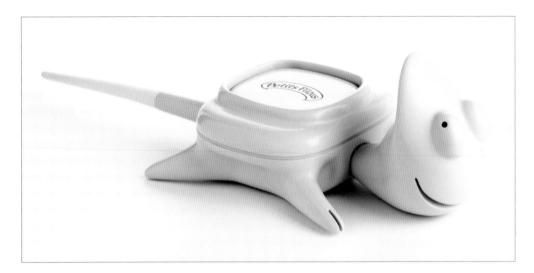

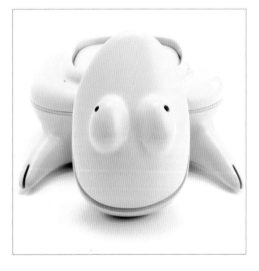

A future concept for Petits Filous' 'Taking On the World' product range. Aimed to satisfy a child's hunger to learn through play and exploration. 'Textures All Around' encourages children to get outside and explore the environment, in search of textures.

The surfaces are replicated into 'tokens' that are collected and later discussed to develop verbal and tactile skills. The product highlights that textures can be seen as well as felt to help develop hand/eye coordination through an honest and less technological characterful product.

Robert Walsh
Industrial Design & Technology BA

Petits Filous Bug Catcher
Future concept for Petits Filous

With rising levels of child obesity in the UK, children are leading unhealthy lifestyles whilst getting little or no exercise. This product tries to encourage children to get outside and explore their natural environments, consequently helping them to lead an active lifestyle.

The conceptual Bug Catcher allows children aged from four to nine years old to explore the outdoors by catching, analysing and learning about bugs.

Post Disciplinary Design
A Manifesto
Joseph Giacomin

There is compelling evidence that design is in the midst of a minor revolution. The market driven years of the 1980s and 1990s have gone and the emphasis is now on a more human-centred agenda. Design in the early 21st century is characterised by a number of striking phenomena including:

- People who are not educated in design are significantly involved in the activity of designing
- The boundaries between traditional products have become blurred
- The edges between historical design disciplines are steadily dissolving and the work of designers now commonly transcend disciplinary borders such as interior design, product design and graphic design
- The focus of much new design is on the experiential rather than the physical or material

Design is a creative activity performed in support of people. As a profession, design has co-evolved together with the society that it serves, from pre-industrial times up to the present day. At each historical stage in its evolution design education and design practice have adapted to the needs of society. From the mass production of essential consumer goods to the conception and branding of goods intended for quality of life enhancement through to today's mass personalisation of products.

As we survey our 21st century horizon it becomes clear that designers no longer fit neatly into distinct specialist categories. Today's rapidly changing social, economic, technological and environmental demands require individuals who are highly flexible and quickly able to adapt to different contexts in order to help create sustainable futures. Recognition of this changed scenario is essential if both design education and design practice are to meet the major challenges that face humanity.

Post Disciplinary Design is a new movement which is characterised by the concepts of multi-curiosity and multi-disciplinary working. Post Disciplinary Design activity seeks knowledge and skills from all professions in support of activity which is performed to enhance people's lives. Multi-curiosity and multi-disciplinary working are all-encompassing and all-inclusive approaches which begin with the careful observation and understanding of people's needs so as to sensitively shape solutions. This general approach creatively and seamlessly mixes relevant knowledge and skills from many sectors in a manner that is appropriate to 21st century endeavours.

Post Disciplinary Design transcends traditional academic and professional boundaries. The emphasis is on the identification of opportunities, and on the solving of problems, using appropriate knowledge and methods from areas such as business studies, computer science, economics, engineering, human factors, management, physical sciences, psychology and the social sciences. Post Disciplinary Design does not recognise barriers and limitations to creative activity in support of people, and it does not limit itself to a specific sector such as fashion, product or graphic design.

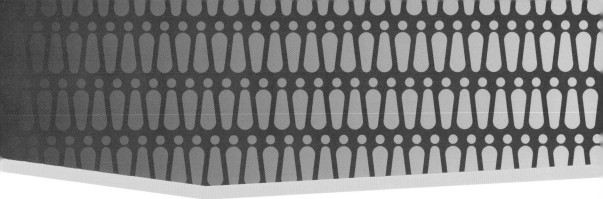

Post Disciplinary Design is a response to the growing need for training and professional practice which can contribute effectively to any area of the modern global economy. It emphasises the many benefits that derive from the combination of a solid grounding in social and technological knowledge, coupled with a strong emphasis on personal expression and creativity. The approach is broadly aligned with modern policy objectives supported by the Cox Review, the Innovation Nation Report and the various documents treating the Creative Industries agenda.

With this manifesto the Post Disciplinary Design Group wishes to clarify its approach to design education and design practice. It is hoped that others will join us in our efforts to establish new knowledge and new practices, which enable the designers of tomorrow to face humanity's future challenges with confidence.

Joseph Giacomin Brunel University
David Harrison Brunel University
Richard Rakowski Brunel University
Paul Rodgers Edinburgh Napier University
Michael Smyth Edinburgh Napier University
Tony Hodgson Loughborough University
Eddie Norman Loughborough University
Tracy Bhamra Loughborough University
Richard Bibb Loughborough University
Cees de Bont TU Delft University
Erik Jan Hultink TU Delft University

Understanding People: The Key to Success in Business and Design

Professor Patrick W. Jordan

Good design should meet people's practical and emotional needs and connect with their values. As designers we have to get to know our users deeply, to understand what motivates them and to understand the role that the product or service that we are designing will play in their lives.

When I work with my clients on new product development, we use a framework called The Four Pleasures. This looks at different aspects of people's lives and helps us to understand their needs in a holistic manner.

The Four Pleasures are:

Physio:
To do with the body and the senses. A product should fit the person using it physically, in terms of ergonomics for example. The product's physical properties, such as it's tactile qualities can also communicate quality.

Psycho:
To do with the mind. The way that a product or service works should be easy to understand. It should also be emotionally engaging and using it should be a positive experience.

Socio:
To do with relationships – concrete relationships, such as those with family, friends, co-workers etc., but also abstract relationships such as socio-economic status. Many products act as social badges reflecting the status and image of the user.

Ideo:
To do with values. People are increasingly buying products that reflect their values and we need to know what these are.

As an example of a product that connects in all four of these ways, think of the Apple iPhone. This is a product which is easy and emotionally engaging to use (psycho); feels great to hold and is ergonomic (physio); is something that attracts attention (socio); and is associated with being modern, creative and successful (ideo).

However, a particular product need not necessarily engage on all four of these areas, in order to be successful, as long as it engages on one or more.

For example, the hybrid car, the Toyota Prius, has been successful because it connects so well with ideo pleasure. In this case the environmental benefits of the vehicle make it extremely attractive to many people who are concerned about the environment. The car's distinctive shape also gives it socio appeal. Because it is so distinctive, other people can immediately tell that you are driving an eco-friendly car.

The socio dimension is likely to be of huge importance in any situation where a service is being offered in a public space. For example, although Starbucks serves great coffee, this is not necessarily the main reason for the success of the brand. As well as serving coffee, the company has created a positive social experience around visiting their restaurants. They call this concept 'The Third Place.' The idea is that the home is the first place in people's lives, work is the second place, and Starbucks aim to be the third place.

The stores are designed to be places where you can go to do some work as you would in the office, or to relax and read the paper, as you would at home. The décor is neutral enough to be reflective of a modern home or a funky office. It is a place to go to work and relax as much as it is a place to have coffee.

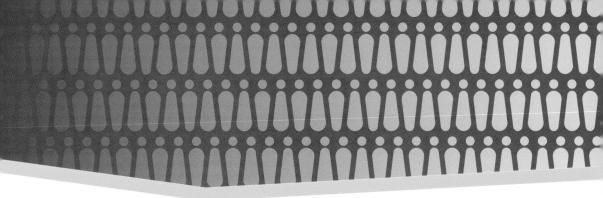

When we give our customers a great user experience, we make them feel good: good about the product or service; good about us; and good about themselves.

Creating products and services that make people feel good about themselves is one of the most important things that we can do as designers. It makes the world a happier and a better place. It will also bring our customers back to us again and again. It is the key to great design and to business success.

Patrick W. Jordan
A Future Thinker

Patrick W. Jordan is a strategic advisor to many of the world's most successful brands as well as to the UK and US governments. For more information see:

www.patrickwjordan.com
www.patrickwjordan.net

Diary of a Creative Entrepreneur

Lisa Tse

I am often asked the same questions.

They usually prompt the same answers.

When faced with limitless choice at the start of your creative career, the prospect of making a decision, however apparently well informed, is perplexing at best.

Six months after graduating from my Masters at Central Saint Martins in 2004, I decided to set up my own signature design studio in London.

I am often told it was a brave and courageous decision to go out on my own.

Having weighed up my worst case scenario which, assuming the business went nowhere, would have been to face defeat and get a job. Hardly petrifying when so analytically justified.

Getting a job was my worst case scenario.

I soon realised that the thought itself was far more daunting than the act.

Indeed, we live in a world where certainty is a stranger and one can spend more time concerned with navigating errors in judgement than observing where our genuine path may lie. Why are we so afraid of getting it wrong?

I soon adapted my approach.

Don't make stupid mistakes. Make clever ones.

I discovered that perpetual perfection served little purpose and that in order to progress we must face up to the challenges that emerge and should we lose, we learn and more importantly, we grow.

I have instinctively known throughout my life that I would end up in a creative career. Like many, when faced with the choices as a young creative with limitless aspirations, it can be hard to know which path will be best suited.

The key is in the question: what is your passion?

If you are not doing it for yourself, don't do it at all.

I have long believed that working in the creative industry is a true privilege. Each day brings the unknown and we can shape our futures, bringing visions to life.

In addition, there is no one way to do anything. Often you will find there are many ways to do nothing.

Expect the unexpected and all will be fine.

I never started out with a plan. Often the best opportunities emerge when you least expect them. The key is to ensure your doors are open so that opportunity can walk in.

My father always reminded me that our destiny is shaped by our own hands.

We carve out the future we seek. The art of pursuit is everything.

So, the real challenge is in discovering what we truly want to do.

Then simply do it.

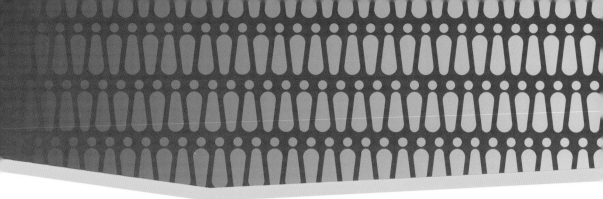

Lisa Tse
Lisa Tse Ltd

Lisa is an international designer and creative businesswoman. She set up her creative agency Lisa Tse Ltd Creative Consulting in 2005 at the age of 26.

In 2008 Lisa, then aged 29, was head hunted for the position of Global Creative Director for The Body Shop, a role she eventually chose not to pursue having chosen to focus on the projects within her own signature agency.

During the Beijing Olympics, Lisa was one of six British delegates on an official Trade Mission to China organised by UK Trade & Investment supported by the British Government, representing the British Design Industry to Chinese businesses. In 2009, Lisa was nominated as one the UK's Top Ten Outstanding Young Chinese. She is also one of five nominated Female Champions for the Addidi 2009 Inspiration Awards for Women Entrepreneurs in association with The Independent on Sunday.

In addition to running her creative agency, Lisa is launching a signature jewellery line in China, Co-Founder of Opus Artz Digital Art Studio and Bloom & Tse Consultancy and also establishing an exclusive women's creative business network.

www.lisatse.com

Michael Abate
Industrial Design BSc

Wind-Up Hearing Aid
Developing hearing aids for developing markets using wind-up technology

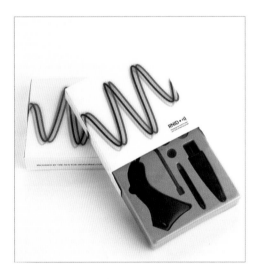

There is a genuine need for effective hearing aids in developing countries. Although aids used in developed countries are being donated, this solution is temporary as developing countries lack the training and facilities to keep these products running.

Designing for developing countries must incorporate several important aspects which include reliability, appropriate power options and easy replacement and repair of components. This project explored possible effective design solutions to implement appropriate hearing aids using wind-up technology. It also looked into developing an infrastructure to provide new employment opportunities to communities and to deliver the training necessary to maintain the hearing aids.

This project was supported by the RNID.

Joe Allum
Industrial Design & Technology BA

Muli
Inclusive cutlery design

This cutlery is inclusively designed to improve and enrich the eating experience of people with reduced grip and dexterity, as well as fully able people, while still maintaining a desirable and stylish cutlery solution.

Myles William Bigden

Product Design BSc

Flipslide
Ankle rehabilitation aid

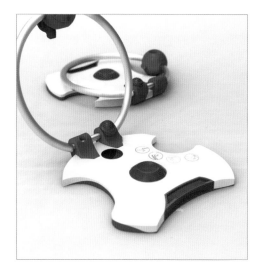

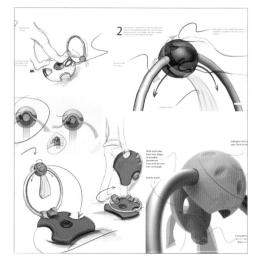

It is estimated that each year 2 million patients are treated for ankle sprains and strains. People that suffer from an ankle injury are more likely to re-injure. Flipslide is a unique exercise product for the home which encourages ankle strengthening during rehabilitation. The product is intuitively designed to promote correct use of the Resistance Band during these exercises.

Flipslide allows exercises to be carried out at home as well as at the physiotherapist's. It provides progress feedback during therapy resulting in a much more engaging experience. This product helps decrease the likelihood of re-injury for those suffering with weak ankles.

Lucy Bradshaw
Industrial Design BSc

Tiny Dreams
Infant sleep soother

Sleep is an essential part of an infant's growth and development, therefore it is one of the most common concerns among parents.

Tiny Dreams transfers the sensory safety of the mother's womb to the outside world. The soft sleeve monitors the infant's movements throughout the night. The characteristics of these movements indicate which sleep stage the infant is progressing through and trigger comforting womb sounds which are played when the child is most likely to wake. The parents' unit provides them with an insight into the infant's sleep patterns, allowing them to experience a deeper understanding of their child.

Alex Bygrave
Industrial Design BSc

Soltan Plus
Providing a unique solution for the prevention of skin cancer

Skin cancer is the most common form of cancer in the UK, accounting for 12,000 new cases each year. Studies have found that a direct link exists between skin cancer and sun exposure, and that around 50% of the UK population does not use sun cream.

In collaboration with the medical physics department of Guy's St Thomas' Hospital, Soltan Plus provides a unique and intuitive solution for the prevention of skin cancer.

It increases public awareness about the dangers of sun exposure and helps people safely manage their time in the sun.

This product is in no way affiliated with Boots or the Boots Soltan brand.

Madeleine Case
Industrial Design BSc

Caterpillar
Child's tilting chair to keep movement in the lower back

In the UK 45% of children have suffered back pain by the age of eleven. Although the chair market has products which claim to help improve posture, these do not solve the problem that our bodies are not intended for sitting, they are designed to move!

The Caterpillar helps children of ages between four and seven to achieve movement during an otherwise sedentary activity.

This ergonomically designed chair has a motor powered tilting system in the seat. The slow tilt of the seat keeps the intervertebral discs and lumbar muscles from stiffening, dramatically reducing the likelihood of developing back pain.

Alan Glazzard

Industrial Design & Technology BA

Balance Bike

A complete system for young children to learn to cycle

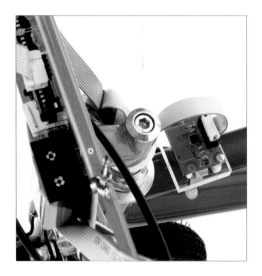

The 'Balance Bike' is a modular learning solution designed to meet the needs of young children aged four to seven years. The bicycle uses a printed circuit board unit to measure leaning and relay appropriate responsive feedback. Auditory feedback is panned between two speakers located on each side of the handlebars, increasing in volume and pitch to whichever side is being leaned on so that corrections in performance can be made. Lean too much, and motors positioned next to each handlebar vibrate to signal to the child to correct their positioning. This inclusion of feedback supports the child in gauging balance tactfully, increases their independence and smoothes the awkward transition of learning to cycle without the need for stabilisers.

Ian Goodhead

Product Design BSc

WaterWing
Rapid response water purification system

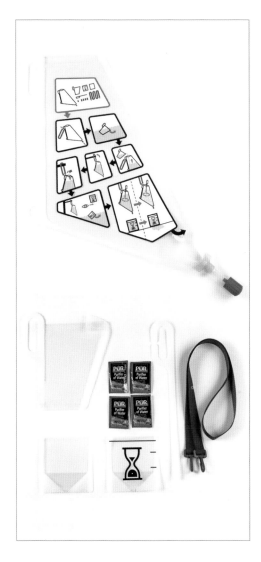

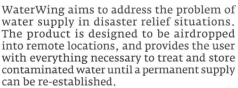

WaterWing aims to address the problem of water supply in disaster relief situations. The product is designed to be airdropped into remote locations, and provides the user with everything necessary to treat and store contaminated water until a permanent supply can be re-established.

The product slows its own descent to ground using a sycamore seed design and expands to become a portable container when filled with water. The product uses P&G's PUR technology to remove both physical and biological contaminants from water and can still be used as a portable container once its purification capacity has been exhausted.

Julien Hadley

Industrial Design BSc

Môme
Self heating nursing bottle

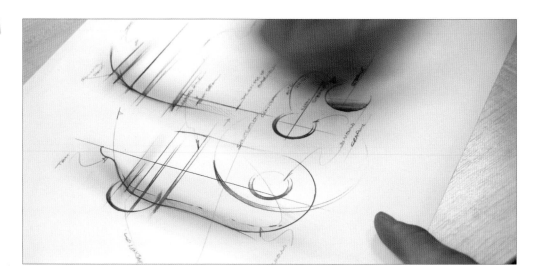

Project Môme began as an investigation into contemporary issues faced by the new parent. Research into psychological and emotional factors as well as the nursing environment showed the need to enhance bottle feeding as an experience.

Môme is a bottle that encourages hygienic user practice during the bottle preparation process. The combination of materials selection and technology give the user assurance that they are providing a safe and satisfying alternative to breast feeding.

Sophie Hibbert
Industrial Design BSc

Reflexion Cosmetic Mirror
Adjustable-focus cosmetic mirror

The NHS estimates that 17.4% of people aged 40 to 45 suffer from long-sightedness. This percentage increases with age as eyesight begins to deteriorate. Long-sighted sufferers have difficulty seeing their mirror image in focus, making it difficult to apply makeup or shave without the aid of their spectacles.

The Reflexion Cosmetic Mirror can be altered to an individual's specific sight requirements, providing an in-focus, magnified image of their face. The mirror eliminates the need for normal vision-correction spectacles which obstruct the face, making it easier to perform personal grooming tasks. Using a pressurised mechanism to control a flexible membrane, the magnification of the mirror can be adjusted until a clear image is obtained.

Marianne Kernohan

Industrial Design BSc

iO

An inclusive radio for people with visual impairments

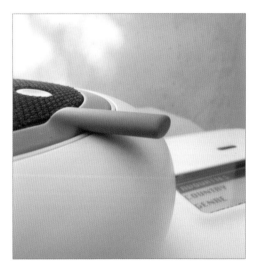

iO is an inclusive solution to the design of an Internet radio based on the needs of people with visual impairments. With over 2 million visually impaired people in the UK, it is important that designers take into account these groups when designing consumer products. With the rapid development of technology it becomes very important to consider usability issues with interfaces on electronic devices. This project explores design interactions using human factors methodology, metaphors and observations alongside close working with a group of visually impaired volunteers using iterative models and prototypes to produce an intuitive and enjoyable product.

Pui-Jun Lam

Industrial Design BSc

Poise

A training device to improve posture during sitting

Back pain and muscular complaints are the most common causes of absence from work in the EU. The problem results in 4.5 million days off work a year. Poise is an electronic training device designed to be used in the workplace to improve posture during sitting and standing.

The product aims to assist the user to maintain a good posture by identifying changes in the geometry of the back and spine, providing the user with instant feedback which leads to immediate correction.

Andrew Liddle

Industrial Design BSc

Breathe-In

Breathing apparatus that provides effective pain relief during early labour

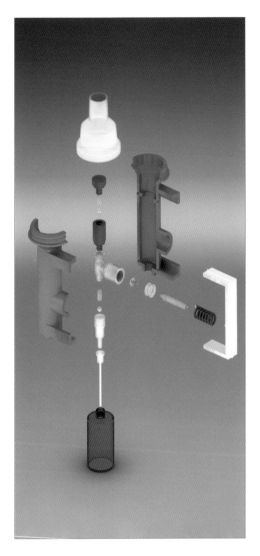

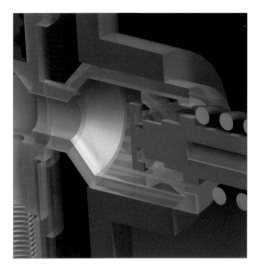

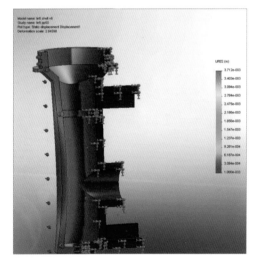

Labour can be one of the most difficult and stressful experiences a woman is ever likely to face. This project explored possible methods of improving the experience.

Research into the current systems and methods of care, coupled with data about people's experiences and expectations, suggested that self control, breathing, calm and stimulation of natural pain-killing endorphins are the most effective means of pain relief during early labour.

This self-regulated aromatherapy-breathing device is designed to operate as a portable nebulizer and uses naturally effective sources to help the user to relax, focus and manage their experience in a more positive manner.

Rebecca McGann
Industrial Design BSc

Isis
Dual-function jewellery piece with mosquito repellent technology

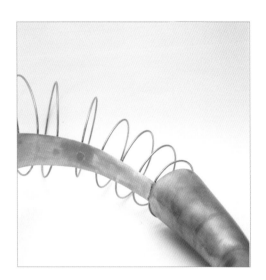 

Few people are unfamiliar with the annoyance of her faint buzzing in their ear, her soft landing upon exposed skin and the tell-tale itchy hives left after her blood meal.

This project is a culmination of years of mosquito hatred.

This solution offers something different from the mosquito repellent options that are currently available: sticky sprays, unattractive wristbands and unreliable electronic devices. Isis is a new product that combines the dual purposes of repelling blood-sucking mosquitoes and providing a powerful, beautiful aesthetic statement for the wearer.

Gary Mitchell
Product Design BSc

Stimulating Alarm Clock
Non-intrusive sleep monitoring system with olfactory dispenser

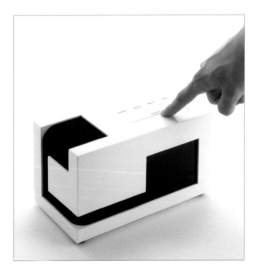

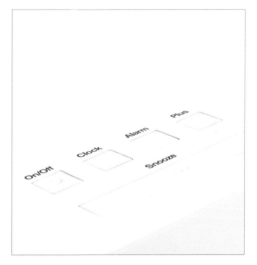

The Stimulating Alarm Clock reduces the feeling of fatigue in the hours following waking, resulting in improved alertness and concentration levels.

The device consists of two systems working in union with each other. A non-intrusive sleep monitoring system that accurately wakes the user during the optimum stage of sleep, in conjunction with an olfactory dispensing system that utilises the psychophysiological effects of essential oils to improve both quality of sleep and the sleep-wake process.

Patrick O'Donoghue
Product Design BSc

Sleep Sense
Reducing the risks of somnambulism

Two percent of the adult population are sleepwalkers. Injurious behaviour is a serious concern for chronic somnambulists. Sleep Sense intelligently monitors movements throughout the house and alerts others if the person is acting unusually. It also calculates the average time an episode begins and then awakens the individual before this time on following nights.

This 'scheduled awakenings' technique is used in clinics to treat sleepwalking. Sleep Sense is aimed at the home medical industry and with no competing products on the market, there is a real potential for this to be given to every diagnosed patient on the NHS for £15.

Kirsten M A Revell

Industrial Design BSc

The Sky Remote - Ergonomic Design Excellence

An exhibition concept for the Design Museum

In November 2009 the Design Museum London will be exhibiting 'Real World Design - How Ergonomics Makes Things Better', an exhibition led by Brunel University to highlight the importance of ergonomics in design to students, professionals and the general public.

Winning an internal competition to produce a concept for this exhibition provided the opportunity to create a 'hands on' engaging exhibit, which appeals particularly to designers and which incorporates best practice in terms of both exhibition design and ergonomics.

User research led to the concept being focused on the TV remote control, and collaboration with Frazer Design, who designed the Sky remote, provided revelations of excellent ergonomic practice in the design process.

Benjamin Scott
Industrial Design BSc

A Crutch Revolution

Innovation of the elbow crutch addressing current adverse effects

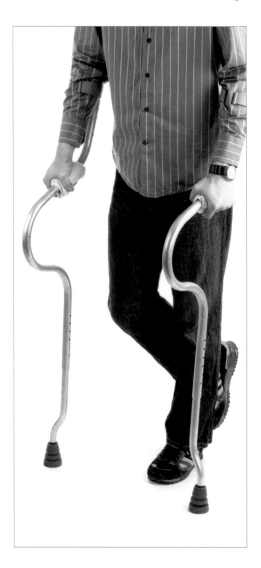

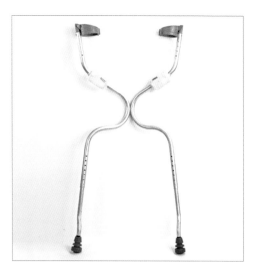

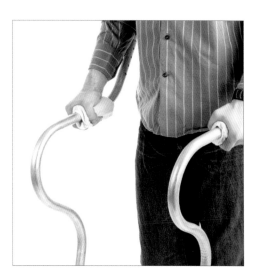

There are medical and physical issues associated with existing elbow crutch designs which need to be addressed and resolved. Walking on crutches requires 2.5 times the amount of energy than that of unaided ambulation. Repetitive impulse loading of the crutch also leads to additional biomechanical injury during use.

The new crutch form is based on the geometry of human motion. Ergonomic handles encourage correct posture of the arms and back during use. Positive feedback is achieved through physical form, and the users' centre of gravity is lowered in order to increase stability. These features combine to produce a more suitable alternative to the current crutch design.

Gareth Scott
Industrial Design & Technology BA

STRIDE
Anterior cruciate ligament knee brace

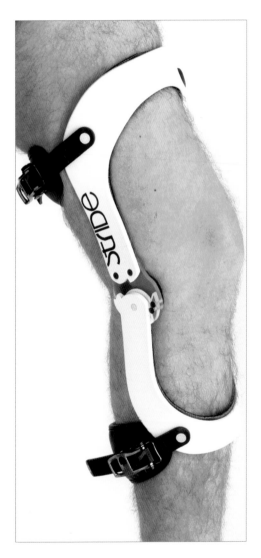

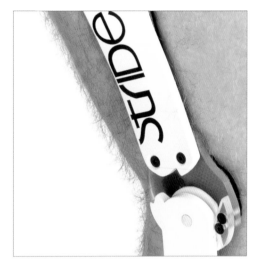

Modern society has evolved the idealism of being fit and healthy, however the time spent on treadmills or running outside has a severe effect on our knees. The amount of knee injuries has been steadily rising over the last decade.

It is commonplace for people to require a knee brace to help rebuild muscles and protect the ligaments for at least two months post operatively. After analysing current knee braces, their various shortcomings were exposed, resulting in a knee brace of enhanced reliability and quality which speeds up recovery.

Kunal Sethi
Industrial Design BSc

Purebreathe Nasal
A nasal air filter that prevents airborne allergy symptoms

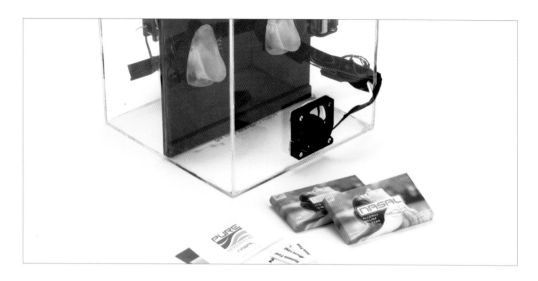

Unfortunately the air we breathe has been, and continues to be, polluted with chemicals as well as naturally occurring particles such as pollen. This contamination accounts for many allergies and illnesses. Products exist on the market which aid in filtering out these particles, however none have been developed to allow the user to guard the respiratory system more comfortably. The Purebreathe Nasal attempts to address the comfort issue with existing nasal air filters and also help people who face a greater health risk from air pollution in a range of environments.

James Vardy
Industrial Design BSc

NX Protection
The crash helmet for your neck

Designed to allow you to walk away from a large accident rather than be air lifted, NX Protection protects against hyperflexion neck injuries. The device suits multiple neck shapes and sizes and is appropriate for skiing, cycling and horse riding. The carefully selected materials protect both the neck and the brain.

NX protection was developed with the assistance of both physiotherapists and biomechanics experts and has been tested both physically and virtually. Usability and value engineering were key to the design process, ensuring that the end user is not alienated or priced out.

Anna West
Industrial Design BSc

Huggle
Be calm under pressure

In the UK approximately 1 in 100 children are affected by an autistic spectrum disorder. Deep pressure is a calming therapy that these children often seek out. The Huggle applies deep pressure using air filled cavities, reducing the internal diameter, and allowing the child to gain the needed therapy in a fun and exciting way.

There are a limited number of products designed for children with autism. This project aimed to design a product that could be used in schools by children of all abilities. It is intuitive to use and, most importantly, it is fun!

Neil Willetts

Industrial Design BSc

LinkMaker

An educational tool for children with autistic spectrum disorders

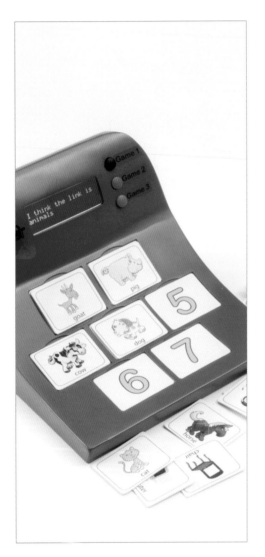

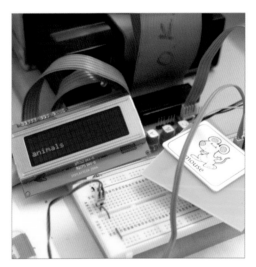

Autism has recently been theorised to be a condition which causes the brain to make too many connections when confronted with sensory stimulation, allowing the savant abilities of some, but causing the reclusive, distant traits of many. By encouraging basic links to be made at a young age, order and knowledge can be bought to otherwise over-stimulating situations.

The LinkMaker helps children with autism establish and remember these links. It works by asking the child to select and place cards which match a theme, or by asking the child to guess the theme of a given set of cards, enforcing the idea of the 'obvious' link.

Courtney Wood
Industrial Design & Technology BA

Hoops
Increasing physical play in the home

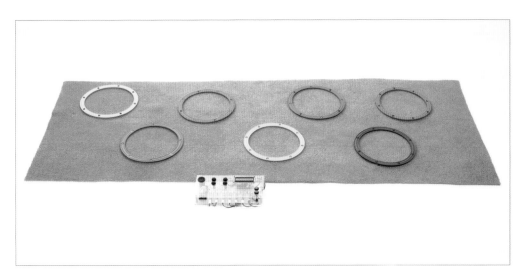

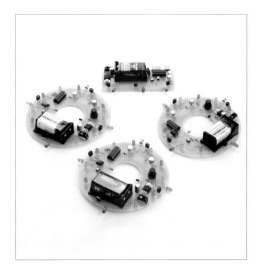

Hoops is an interactive game that encourages children to become active inside the home. Seven rings light up in a random sequence, and the player is required to jump from lit ring to lit ring to build up a score.

Five games can be played by one or two players. One of the games allows the players to create there own rules, generating imaginative play. Incremental levels of difficulty make the game easy to learn but hard to master.

Daniel Worboys

Industrial Design BSc

Purebreathe - Urban Velo

A respiratory protection device designed for the Chinese urban commuter

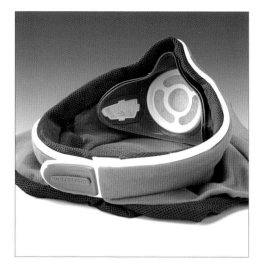

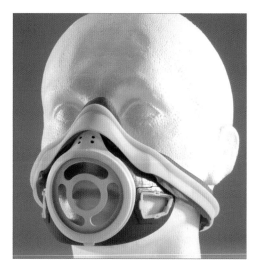

Urban Velo is a respiratory protection device which was developed in collaboration with Lifelab Innovations. It combats industry approved respiratory masks that provide inadequate anthropometric sizing, resulting in reduced air pollution protection for Chinese users. The design incorporates user perceptions to reduce social stigma and improve social acceptance amongst the specific target market.

The design presents an effective and non-intrusive form of air protection within specific environmental conditions.

Extensive biometric and human factor research was conducted to evaluate typical user performance parameters and requirements. The results were used to develop an innovative filtering technology to provide a moisture controlled low resistance filter, with high efficiency particulate protection within a fashion orientated form.

Don't Worry, Be Happy

A guide to positive thinking for the recession

Rebecca McGann

Re.ces.sion (n.)
1. The act of withdrawing or going back.
2. An extended decline in business activity, typically two consecutive quarters of falling gross national product.

The word 'recession' is explained using the latter of these two definitions; as a precise term relating to a company or business' financial performance. The trouble is, widespread experience of this evokes the former definition by way of response. Focused on the doom and gloom of the 'downfall', we enter into a vicious cycle of negativity that in itself is the enemy of creativity...

So is this really the End as we know it? Is the current economic crisis bullying the creative industries into submission? Actually, no. By generating excitement and identifying opportunities, design holds the power to propel us into prosperity once more.

This sort of thinking is not new: times of financial adversity have oft been a source of stimulation for the creative industries, as for creativity in all walks of life. In these times it is human nature and the desire for survival that drives innovation. Think post Wall Street Crash, when prolific industrial designer Raymond Loewy convinced an entire nation that they needed a sleek, sexy, new wave of domestic products. He reinvigorated consumers and the economy in turn, hauling the country out of the recession almost single-handedly.

Taking a look at the next serious American depression in 1981, fashion designers nationwide such as Vivienne Westwood encouraged the masses to 'Dress to impress', spawning power dressing trends such as larger-than-life shoulder pads and bright, sharp suits. As ridiculous as some of these trends seem today, the fashion industry responded to a time of economic hardship with admirable boldness and creativity.

Today's fashion designers are acutely aware of the relevance of this, as Riccardo Tisci, creative director for Givenchy testifies: "But the world has so many problems- in war, in banks –and, like in the Eighties, fashion has to be powerful and strong at a time of social crisis. It's not about creating trends that can just be copied, but creating an identity that is clear".

More recently, industrial design companies with a high culture of success have withstood economically difficult periods in the 1990s: American design consultancy IDEO in particular has nurtured an environment that is conducive to constant innovation and invigoration. Their positive working attitudes and understanding of its importance to a company's success has been key to their success.

They channel huge amounts of energy into keeping the team fresh and productive, and at the heart of this is passion: One chapter in their homegrown business bible 'The Art of Innovation' is titled 'Generating your own Energy'. This and maintaining a positive outlook are synonymous, as Tom Kelley explains "Peters cheers us all on to turn our work into 'wow projects'. Something you're proud of. Something that makes a difference. Something you can tell your kids about."

The power of positive thinking has not gone unnoticed by psychologists either. The area is well documented and research has been undertaken into the science of optimism, hope and creativity and their effects on human behaviour.

Optimism is thought to have a profound effect on the goal-achieving capacity of an individual: "Scheier and his colleagues argue that optimistic people, in the face of difficulties, continue to pursue their valued goals and regulate themselves and their personal states using effective coping strategies so that they are likely to achieve their goals" (Carr, A., 2004 Positive Psychology, p82. Brunner-Routledge).

Put simply, this is the concept that if you believe you are capable of meeting your target, you are more likely to do so in reality.

Perhaps this is something we could all learn from in this economically difficult time: things aren't easy, but we're certainly not going to make things better with a 'glass half empty' attitude.

Today's consumers are unlikely to be tempted by a new design fad like the one that captured 1930s America and we must not be naïve enough to think this would work second time round. The public at large is increasingly aware, and weary, of the pressures of consumerism.

We need to find our own ways to re-inject some excitement into our lives, our businesses and our society at large. As times have changed, we need a different design philosophy to ignite the public's interest; products need to be more intuitive, more considered and 'intelligent'. Technological advances have increased the 'personalisation' of users' experiences, and so mass-market consumer goods are no longer enough.

It will take an innovative thinker to pave the way for a resurgence of consumer excitement; but this needn't revolve around big revolutionary ideas that take huge amounts of time and money to fulfil. Instead, perhaps we should focus on smaller, day-to-day innovations that could have just as much impact, introducing a culture of healthy competition to stimulate creativity. However best to tackle the recession, some positive thinking would be a good place to start.

So what are the key recession-busting tips of the moment? It has been proved that innovating during difficult economic times can hold the key to success and a ticket out of the doom-and-gloom. This is easier said than done, but the power of looking positively towards the future can go a long way; it's been proved in practice, through the likes of Raymond Loewy, Tom Kelley and the guys at IDEO. It's been consolidated by tangible research in the field of positive psychology.

But why not finish with the man of the moment; not a designer, but someone who has instilled long-lost optimism and hope into the lives of millions of people worldwide. Barack Obama defied pessimists everywhere by becoming America's first black president and his unguarded optimism has captured the imaginations of millions. When he won the democratic presidential primary in South Carolina, he challenged cynics who doubted America could change for the better, displaying a fierce, captivating positivity that we could all learn from:

"Yes, we can. Yes, we can change. Yes, we can".

A full version of this essay is available at: www.madeinbrunel.com

Incomunicación ƒ, /ínkə mjùnikáciən/

(nr) lack of communication; isolation; (jur) solitary confinement

Pedro Pineda

It is felt in modern society that people are becoming less and less aware of each other, deepening in a culture of individualism and social isolation. Our modern individualism claims to freely pursue personal goals and well being without restrictions by our peers. Why is it that in big cities so many people feel lonely? Matt Smith from The Viral Factory explains "What London does not have sometimes is a sense of community because we're all so busy doing what we're doing. Everyone has their heads down" (Icon, 2005) This way of life has drawbacks and opportunities. In the current situation it appears that this individualism is creating serious problems in the wellbeing of society, as it seems that people can no longer help each other to overcome problems, or work together for common causes; we seem to be unable to communicate with each other.

So, What is Communication Anyway?

Communication is in itself a package of signals where each one reinforces the others. Our words, the medium, the gestures that go with it, all affect the meaning of messages for the other person. In "the new people making", Satir highlights the importance of communication, "Once a human being has arrived on this earth, communication is the largest single factor determining what kind of relationships she or he makes with others and what happens to them in the world around. How we manage survival, how we make sense, how we connect with our own divinity, all depends largely on our communication skills".

Our Environment, Our Communication?

Communication is the base for any relationship between peers, at the same time it determines us as individuals, hence the types of communication and the quality of it will determine many of our characteristic features.

The way we support open-ness changes radically from one culture to another, but being non judgemental and giving credibility to others makes a huge difference in the confidence they will have to open up to us. To be able to give this credibility is essential to recognize, as well as the differences.

Communication is Basic for Social Capital

Networks make things happen, they allow us to contact the right friend at the right moment for help. This is usually less stressful, faster and typically with better outcomes compared to "established procedures" which normally constrain or patronise us. Healthy networking should allow people to pursue their goals and help connect societies together. Patterns of interaction are changing; many writers and sociologists have expressed their concerns with the mode of day to day interactions and the quality of interpersonal relationships, we seem to be talking past one another rather than to one another. This society is formed by individuals focusing on their own needs, not realizing that being connected is a resource in itself !

How can it be Sparked?

Writers, intellectuals, and activists are talking about a new era, about the power of cooperation, about the capacity for innovation when many people are able to add their insight, about the mass creativity, about the open-source culture, about the desire from millions of people to change their role from passive to active, …, an era of connectivity. Charles Leadbeater in his book WE-THINK talks about the web and its capacity to change the way we work and share ideas. He says that it is appealing in part because it brings back to life more communal and collaborative ways of working, which were sidelined by the industrial organisations from the 20th century. The communication between millions and millions of people is "in principle, giving the capacity for solving shared problems by allowing us to combine the knowledge and insights of millions of people, creating a collective intelligence on a scale never before possible, encouraging us to see everyone as a potential participant in the creation of collaborative solutions through large self-organized networks. The more connected we are, the richer we should be". We-Think is based on sharing, participation, recognition and mutual consideration Nevertheless, best of all is that the web is allowing us to do our leisure hobbies and at the same time help other people and receive recognition for it. This sharing and mutuality adds a much bigger scope for creativity and ideas to flourish. And, as Leadbeater says, "Shared and mutuality can be as effective base for productive activities as private ownership"

Can it be done in our Public Life?

Is this cooperation just possible through the digital media? Is there not an "analogue" version to the web? Well, the web is a tool, a medium used by humans, and the desires plausible in their web life, are desires in their physical-public life.

The common factor of all these activities is the desire for participation, the desire to play an active role, and it comes from people that are doing their hobbies. There is pleasure and enjoyment which results in a happier life, and because it is done just for pleasure there is no need for rules or constrains.

People object that some will take advantage of it and over use it or misuse the resources. EXCUSES!

This method is based on communication between peers on mutual criticism and consideration. Trust in each others willing to do their best.

Spaces where communication is sparked foster a spirit of collaboration. What is clear is that isolated creativity will get us nowhere. Communication is a two way activity, not just about saying but also about listening.

We, the Creative People , No Excuses, We are all Creative People!

Let's not wait for the perfect time or the right situation, let's experiment, discover, let's be curious. We have more possibilities than ever to work together in new ways, to spark mass-creativity and mass contributions; and it is up to us, tools are tools and will do nothing without our human input behind them. Give tools and motivation to the people so that they can contribute, but bear in mind all the basics for a We-Think culture: sharing, participation, recognition and mutual consideration. It should not be "I and They", where we rely on excuses like "it is not my fault!" or "I can't change anything!", but a 'We' culture based on communication where we inspire each other to contribute by doing our part and welcoming theirs. Seeing people as a resource we can create a spontaneous independent yet interrelated society, a lifestyle that encourages interaction and opinions, sparks creativity and where anybody can communicate an idea to anybody else.

We are all unique; we can all put our unique part in this world combining thoughts that are different but complementary. At the end, communication isn't about technology, languages, or culture. Communication is about giving an opportunity to others and ourselves to express, is about infecting people with a good idea and encouraging this to happen.

A full version of this essay is available at: www.madeinbrunel.com

MA Design Strategy Research

Laura Bentley
MA Design & Branding Strategy

Bonding through branding: localising internal branding experiences

Globalisation of business, developing economies and innovative technology are creating an increasingly flat, highly competitive and borderless world. A loyal and engaged employee base is a key competitive advantage. My aim is to design an emotional internal branding framework that localises the brand experience for international employees of multi-national corporations to increase loyalty.

Jaclyn A. Immordino
MA Design & Branding Strategy

BRANDcentricity: Redesigning organisations around their brand for holistic performance improvement

A contemporary approach to business management, Brandcentricity stems from an idea to incorporate design strategy and management strategy to redesign organisations systemically for increased profitability. Design thinking can change the way that companies operate and will change the way that we do business in every field, especially holistic performance improvement consulting.

Renato Kern

MA Design & Branding Strategy

A narrative framework to create brand personality

This research project aims to design a framework to create brand personality through using creative writing and character creation techniques. The unique aspect is that it is conceptualized as a multidisciplinary project which merges different creative strands (the rubber band metaphor) together to create a personal emotional relationship between consumers and brands.

Ivan Tuen

MA Design & Branding Strategy

Persuasive Design : A new framework for the NPD process

This research will establish a new framework for delivering persuasiveness through the idea generation stage of new product development for both product and services, specifically in the area of green and sustainable living. By entering the "consumer black box" and evaluating real motivations, the process will heighten the integration of innovation, branding and design.

Chen Yue
MA Design & Branding Strategy

Enhancing Children's Dentistry: Design strategy for reducing fear and improving health

This research project seeks to enhance children's dental health through conveying positive emotional experiences in dentistry by using cartoon characters.

By investigating children's responses to dental treatment and their interpretation of cartoon characters, the strategy will reduce their fear and improve their dental health.

Image based on Toothbeary Dental Practice

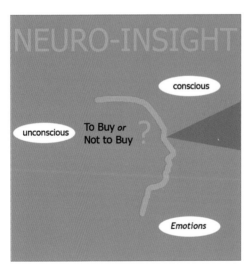

Shaun Nigel Myles
MA Design & Branding Strategy

NEURO-INSIGHT for Innovation: Uncovering hidden consumers needs

Traditional consumer research still finds it difficult to predict possible take-up of new brands or brand elements. People struggle to articulate how they think and feel about brands – even very familiar ones.

This project uses Future Forecasting to identify likely adoption of neuroscience into mainstream brand theory and practice, and to identify the impact on the Design / Branding process.

Rafael Mello
MA Design & Branding Strategy

**What you get is what you see
Designing a brand strategy for new mobile
communications**

Regarding the new mobile technologies and
the 3G internet protocol, new market gaps
emerge. Considering the customers' opinions
and insights from market professionals,
the research aim is to create a design and
branding strategy based on the concept of
mass customisation in order to improve the
mobile phone customer experience.

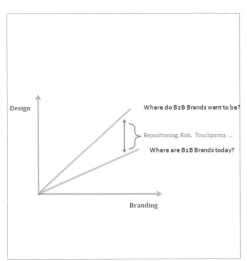

Jung-Yeon Jang
MA Design & Branding Strategy

**Using creative and strategic design for B2B
building a strong brand for the business-
to-business sector**

Increasingly, creative designs are recognised
as strategic assets, as they generate profits
and secure business sustainability. Despite
the intensive use of creative designs in
branding processes in the Business-to-
Consumer sectors, most B2B companies
currently overlook the potential power of
creative designs. As a result, my research
aims to create design strategies to help B2B
businesses utilise creative designs in their
brands developments.

MA Design Strategy Research

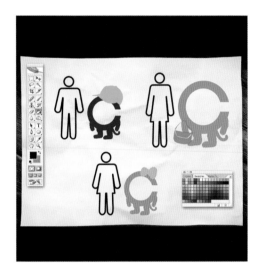

Surapen Yosravikul

MA Design & Branding Strategy

The Character and the Brand

This research investigates the role of characters in branding and develops a new strategy for designing characters which represent the personality of brands. It will offer a tool for brand managers, designers and advertisers to select suitable characters and effectively communicate brand identity and personality.

Jea Hoo Na

MA Design Strategy & Innovation

What Next? Future of product based UK design consultancies

This research will seek to answer the ubiquitous yet fundamental question of the future for UK product based design consultancies by analysis of professional opinions and theories in design strategy. It will focus on the importance of strategic and business thinking in design industry to prosper amidst increasing global competition.

Creating an Innovative Culture

Eilis McNulty

MA Design Strategy & Innovation

Creating an innovative culture: The future direction of Irish design consultancies

This research project investigates the value of design-led innovation as a strategic future model for Irish design consultancies. Within the design sector globalisation has resulted in a shift in the industry's dynamics, requiring a more holistic approach to design. My aim is to provide a future direction for Irish design consultancies, which will enable them to adapt to the changing marketplace and become more competitive internationally through differentiation.

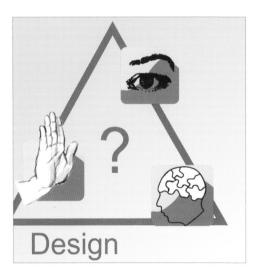

Design

Iraklis Georgiadis

MA Design Strategy & Innovation

Triangulation: Collaborations between the design industry, the design profession and design academia

This research project explores collaborations between the Design Industry, Design Academia and the Design Profession. The aim is to show how critical design thinking can strengthen current interactions by identifying perception gaps, knowledge transfer and stress-points. The over-arching argument is to strengthen the triangle, and the ultimate beneficiary is the world at large.

MA Design Strategy Research

No one trashes now there are flowers!! - experiential influence

Koogin Han
MA Design Strategy & Innovation

Experiential Design Leadership: Improving communication and leadership for modern multidisciplinary project development.

My research is about creating a model for Multidisciplinary Design Project Leadership utilising 'experiential design methods' to improve communication and leadership effectiveness.

Exploring the concept of experience and the process of learning ultimately suggests designers as leaders in influencing strategic directions of new project developments.

Antoine Gripay
MA Design Strategy & Innovation

French Furniture Design Strategy: Repositioning firms to challenge the global market

This research project explores the declining furniture industry in France. The aim is to create a design strategy which integrates design thinking and branding into businesses. The final achievement is to re-position business through differentiation in the global market and challenge the low-cost competition.

Tsinghua University, China

Renhua Du

Healthcare Trolley for Children

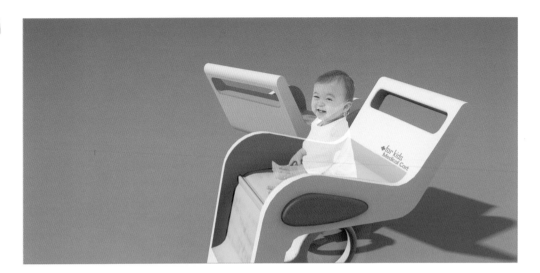

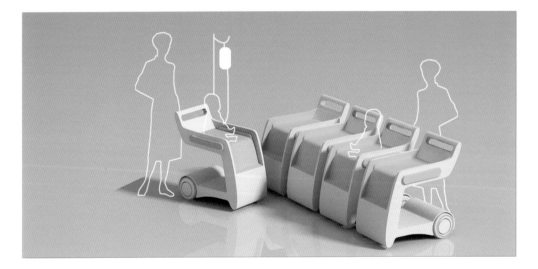

This mobile medical bed is designed for one to five year old children to help ease their fear of hospitals. This fear can cause problems for both parents and doctors. To combat this, the trolley has been designed in a bright, eye-catching colour and an emotive shape.

Children will feel at ease in the hospital when resting on this trolley and this will result in happier and more confident parents.

Spring is the peak season for children to see a doctor in China. Hospitals may sometimes run out of medical beds, however, since the traditional medical bed occupies too much space. This new trolley addresses this important issue by being compact and light, thus saving highly valuable hospital space.

Tsinghua University, China
Zhang Hui

Future Living Concept

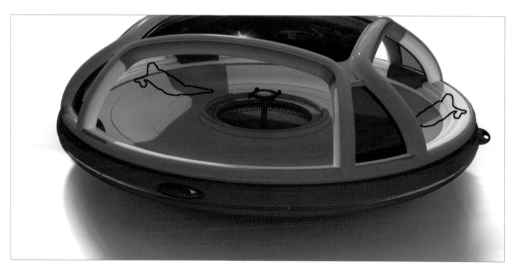

A Future living concept, exploring new ideas
for socio-physical well-being.

Tsinghua University, China

Jiawei Gu

iTilta
A uniquely designed wheelchair

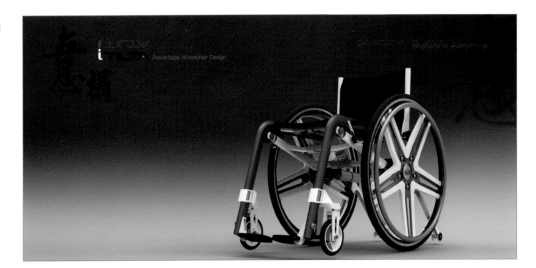

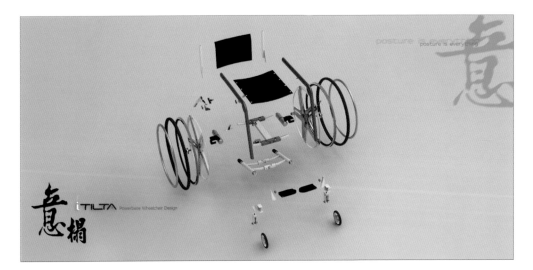

iTilta is a wheelchair with a unique structure. Designed for independently minded and adaptable users, it is fully adjustable, ultra light weight and engineered for modern urban life. Due to its elastic structure, with pressure transmission tappet, it allows the user to maintain their chosen, ideal posture. iTilta provides ease of ingress and egress and incorporates adjustment of the sitting height so as to match adjoining surfaces.

iTilta trnsforms medical engineering aesthetics in order to achieve a more friendly and sociable user interface.

Tsinghua University, China

Junn Li

The Public Bicycle Rental System

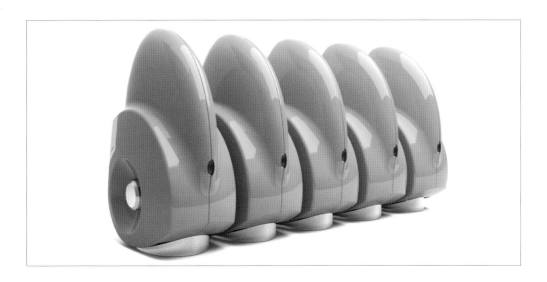

One of the problems in a big city like Beijing is the lack of land resources. In the design of the Public Bicycle Rental System. The design objective is to achieve minimal land occupancy while simultaneously developing an aesthetically pleasing and harmonious form.

Tsinghua University, China

Qing Liu

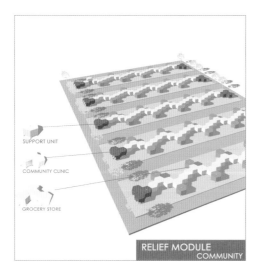

SUPPORT UNIT

COMMUNITY CLINIC

GROCERY STORE

RELIEF MODULE
COMMUNITY

A new concept in prefabricated architectural design which explores modularity as a means of achieving flexibility of construction, versatility of use and physical well-being.

Wendy
Experience 'camera' for the visually impaired

As society becomes more complex and life more fast paced visually impaired people can feel more in need of assistance. Sharing experiences with friends can become increasingly difficult. The project enables the visually impaired to explore the outside World, whilst simultaneously recording the experience.

Wendy is quite different from a traditional 'white cane' due to its interchangible head unit. When using the microphone recorder, the visually impaired are able to record events in the same way that somebody else might use a digital camera. This allows them to replay the event so as to share their experiences with friends.

Extended
Network

Partners

Tsinghua University
Academy of Arts and Design

Tsinghua University, established in 1911, is one of China's foremost comprehensive research universities. At present, the University has 13 schools and 55 departments with faculties in science, engineering, humanities, law, medicine, history, philosophy, economics, management, education and art. The University has now over 25,900 students, including 13,100 undergraduates and 12,800 graduate students. As one of China's most renowned universities, Tsinghua has become an important institution for fostering talent and scientific research.

The educational philosophy of Tsinghua is to "train students with integrity". Among over 120,000 students who have graduated from Tsinghua since its founding are many outstanding scholars, eminent entrepreneurs and great statesmen remembered and respected by their fellow Chinese citizens.

With the motto of "Self-Discipline and Social Commitment" and the attitude of "Actions Speak Louder than Words", Tsinghua University is dedicated to the well-being of Chinese society and to world development.

Indian Institute
of Technology Madras

Indian Institute of Technology Madras is one of the premier institutions of national importance in higher technical education and basic and applied research. It was established in 1959 by the Government of India in collaboration with assistance from the German Government.

The Institute has developed considerable academic infrastructure and earned an international reputation for excellence in education. The Institute has sixteen academic departments and a number of advanced research centres in various disciplines of engineering and pure sciences, with nearly 100 laboratories organised in a unique functioning pattern. It is a residential institution with almost 460 faculty members, approximately 4500 students and 1250 administrative supporting staff.

A faculty of international repute, a brilliant student community, excellent technical and supporting staff, as well as an effective administrative team have all contributed to the preeminent status of IIT Madras. The campus is located in the city of Chennai, previously known as Madras. Chennai is the state capital of Tamil Nadu, a southern state in India.

IIT Madras is committed to the advancement of knowledge through education and research, in both Pure and Applied Science, and within Engineering, Social Sciences and Humanities. The vision of IIT Madras is "To be an academic institution in dynamic equilibrium with its social, ecological and economic environment striving continually for excellence in education, research and technological service to the nation".

Rhode Island
School of Design

Rhode Island School of Design
is a global leader in educating creative
people who aspire to make a meaningful
contribution to our world.

Rhode Island School of Design (RISD)
was founded in 1877 in Providence,
Rhode Island and is a vibrant community
of artists and designers that includes
2,200 students from around the world,
approximately 350 faculty and curators,
plus 400 staff members.In addition, each
year more than 200 prominent artists,
critics, authors and philosophers visit
the historic College Hill campus.

The mission of the Rhode Island School
of Design, through its college and museum,
is to educate its students and the public
in the creation and appreciation of
works of art and design, to discover
and transmit knowledge and to make
lasting contributions to a global
society through critical thinking,
scholarship and innovation.

Simon Fraser University
Interactive Arts and Technology

Named after an explorer, Simon Fraser,
SFU opened in 1965. Taking only 30 months
to grow from the idea stage into an almost
completed campus with 2,500 students
it was dubbed the "Instant University".

Just over 42 years later SFU has over 30,000
students and 100,000 alumni, more than
700 tenure-track faculty and 1,600 staff.
The original campus has grown into three
vibrant campuses in Burnaby, Vancouver
and Surrey and SFU's reputation has grown
into one of innovative teaching, research
and community outreach.

Brunel University's School of Engineering
and Design is particularly pleased
to welcome Simon Fraser's renowned School
of Interactive Arts and Technology to the
Made in Brunel family in 2009.

Courses at Brunel University
School of Engineering and Design

Design

Brunel Design represents the best of creative thinking with innovations making use of new materials, emerging technologies, and advanced methods. At the heart of our work is the fundamental need to design innovative new products with empathy for the targeted users. We design for people; so many of the exciting ideas within this book have been initially generated by users, developed together and realised appropriately. Brunel Design embodies the synergy of all these aspects of innovation and this Made in Brunel book contains the very best graduating design practitioners.

The family of Brunel Design degree courses allows young design thinkers to explore their creative potential, develop competence in technological understanding and apply business knowledge to product development. Our Design graduates have the most comprehensive portfolios of transferable skills. Strong relationships with manufacturing and service companies across the globe enable us to align our teaching to the constantly evolving needs of industry. All of the courses benefit from real projects set by industrial partners and over 90% of our undergraduates have gained professional and cultural experience through their year working in industry or abroad on industrial placements.

Undergraduate Design courses:
- Industrial Design & Technology BA
- Product Design BSc
- Product Design Engineering BSc

Postgraduate Design:
- 4 specialist MA and MSc courses

Admissions Tutor:
Stephen Green
stephen.green@brunel.ac.uk

Electronic & Computer Engineering

The subject area encompasses a broad variety of courses that focus on today's connected digital society. We develop the engineers, technologists and designers who will arc hitect and implement the means of this technological revolution. Our courses have strong links with industry; students conduct 'live' assignments on briefs set by industrial partners. Many students choose to participate in an industrial placement and have worked at companies like Walt Disney, Microsoft, Avid, Xerox, Dare Digital and many others, often gaining their first job with their placement employer.

Undergraduate Electronic & Computer Engineering courses:
- Broadcast Media (Design & Technology) BSc
- Communication Networks Engineering BEng/MEng
- Computer Systems Engineering BEng/MEng
- Electrical Engineering with Renewable Energy Systems MEng
- Electronic & Computer Engineering MEng
- Electronic & Electrical Engineering (Communication Systems) BEng/MEng
- Electronic & Electrical Engineering BEng/MEng
- Electronic & Microelectronic Engineering BEng
- Internet Engineering BEng
- Mobile Computing BSc
- Multimedia Technology & Design BSc
- Networked Media Engineering BEng/MEng

Postgraduate Electronic & Computer Engineering:
- 6 Specialist MSc courses

Admissions Tutor:
Professor John Stonham
john.stonham@brunel.ac.uk

Mechanical Engineering

Engineering plays a key role within modern society in generating technological innovations and providing exciting career opportunities. The mechanical engineering students who feature in Made in Brunel demonstrate the intellect, creativity and industry-relevant skills required to succeed within their chosen professions. The project work on display from mechanical engineering underlines our commitment to innovation and excellence. Some of these projects are team-based and highlight the benefits of cooperative working so important to contemporary global industry.

Undergraduate Mechanical Engineering courses:

- Aerospace Engineering BEng/MEng
- Aviation Engineering BEng/MEng
- Aviation Engineering with Pilot Studies BEng/MEng
- Civil Engineering with Sustainability BEng/MEng
- Mechanical Engineering (with Aeronautics, with Automotive Design or with Building Services) BEng/MEng
- Motorsport Engineering BEng/MEng

Postgraduate Mechanical Engineering:

- 9 Specialist MSc courses

Admissions Tutor:

Petra Gratton
petra.gratton@brunel.ac.uk

West London Innovation
Industry - University Networking

The quadrant of London sweeping out from Kensington and Chelsea, which encompasses Wembley Stadium, Heathrow Airport, the Thames, M4 and M40 corridors travelling westwards is one of the most economically successful and vibrant regions in the world. West London comprises more than 750,000 jobs and 67,000 businesses, which in 2004 contributed £27 billion to the UK economy. Heathrow, the world's most successful airport, is a natural global hub for the world. The region has a tremendous track record as a home for innovative business at the cutting edge of global markets including the likes of GSK, BA, Disney, Diageo and BSkyB.

At Made in Brunel a number of organisations have come together to promote the considerable opportunities and potential of collaborating between business and Universities, to ally the research and knowledge available with the entrepreneurial spirit of the area.

West London Partnership

The chief executives and leaders of the six local authorities and senior staff both from large corporate businesses and from SMEs based in West London join forces as WLP to develop the overall social and economic interests of the region. This dynamic partnership has a broad remit including transport, regeneration, skills and workforce development, planning and property, spatial development and housing.

www.westlondonpartnership.org

London Development Agency

Strong links exist between the LDA, tasked with developing the London economy, and organisations in the West London region promoting and managing numerous practical funding initiatives that exist to support and develop innovation, skills and knowledge.

www.lda.gov.uk

West London Business

Whatever your size and whatever your sector, West London Business can help your business grow and compete. With a series of top quality business information and networking events, a strong lobbying and representation profile and a membership brimming with businesses from across the sub-region, West London Business is the premier business network.

www.westlondon.com

WestFocus

A consortium of seven universities. located in South and West London and the Thames Valley (including Brunel University), WestFocus encourages the flow of knowledge and resources between higher education, business and the wider community. It helps companies and individuals to solve their business problems through a range of activities, from funding for high technology spin-outs to training and business advice.

www.westfocus.org.uk

Designplus

Part of the Westfocus network, Designplus represents design interests and facilitates events, training and collaborative projects in all aspects of design, particularly within important emerging areas such as design for health, wearable technology and human centered design.

www.designplus.org.uk

CITIN
Creative Industries Technology and Innovation Network

The Creative Industries Technology and Innovation Network mission is to accelerate innovation in the Creative Industries in the UK. CITIN is home to innovators from all sectors of the Creative Industries from Advertising to Fashion and Design, from Architecture to New Media, TV, Games and beyond. Sharing knowledge and stimulating innovation are vital to the economy. CITIN plays a key role in accelerating innovation within this dynamic business sector. Join our network for free at www.citin.org

Be Inspired
Discover exciting technological and innovative developments in the creative industries.

Get connected
Make the most of opportunities to network with like-minded people, meet potential partners and develop collaborations in the creative industries.

Access support
Identify scope for funding and secure platforms for innovation.

Shape the future
Realise the potential of the creative industries to stimulate lasting change.

Unlocking Potential
Knowledge Transfer Partnerships (KTPs) and the Knowledge Catalyst scheme offer great opportunites for creative businesses and organisations to improve their competitiveness by tapping into expertise and skills from across UK academic institutions.

Funded by the Technology Strategy Board, Research Councils and others, these schemes are focused upon generating innovation in the form of new products and services by supporting a strategic partnership between centres of expertise and businesses. They can provide an important and catalytic link between new and emerging technologies and creative businesses innovation.

However, from CITIN's initial scoping work it appears that the UK's Creative Industries are not taking full advantage of KTPs at the same level as other sectors. Jeremy Davenport, deputy director of CITIN who will lead the programme, said: "We recognize the capacity KTPs have to drive innovation into businesses and act as a catalyst for their growth. We want to ensure that the Creative Industries benefit from these great opportunities."

CITIN has already identified potential to increase uptake among Creative Industries. Some of the issues which appear to be inhibiting business engagement include a lack of awareness of KTPs, the offer from the funders being too big for very small businesses, or KTPs being perceived as an administrative burden.

Jeremy added that the KTN will work to support a community of interest to generate and share insights, knowledge and case studies. There will also be a number of collaborative events focusing on KTPs and the creation of material to demonstrate the tangible benefits that KTPs can bring to the Creative Industries as the basis for promoting the scheme.

This CITIN project comes at the same time as funding for KTPs has been increased and the Technology Strategy Board is introducing a new shorter KTP programme that may appeal to micro and small businesses.

Further details about KTPs are available at www.citin.org

Acknowledgements

Creating this book depends on the extraordinary support of so many busy people. Our sincere thanks to the whole Made in Brunel team, the staff from the School of Engineering and Design, our business partners and the many individuals and companies across the world who have made this innovative publication possible.

Thank you to you all.

Index &
Contacts

Michael Abate
Industrial Design BSc

t: +44 (0)7791 954273
e: mjabate@gmail.com
w: www.abatedesign.co.uk

 122   240

Michael Allen
Motorsport Engineering MEng

e: michael.allen@brunelracing.co.uk

 92

Joe Allum
Industrial Design & Technology BA

t: +44 (0)7875 331090
e: mulidesign@hotmail.com

24   241

Filipe Almeida
Industrial Design & Technology BA

t: +44 (0)7939 531351
e: jesusalmeida86@hotmail.com

 230

Lloyd Axten
Industrial Design & Technology BA

t: +44 (0)7800 574260
e: lloydaxten@hotmail.co.uk
w: www.lloydaxten.co.uk

216

Laura Bentley
Design & Branding Strategy MA

e: laura@freckledesign.com
w: www.freckledesign.com

270

Inderpal Bhogal
Multimedia Technology & Design BSc

t: +44 (0)7763 698282
e: Indy.b@hotmail.co.uk

 134

Myles William Bigden
Product Design BSc

t: +44 (0)7527 087004
e: myles@tstudio.co.uk
w: www.mylesbigden.com

 42   242

Adrian Bisek
Simon Fraser University

t: +1 604 780 8348
e: amb@adrianbisek.com
w: www.adrianbisek.com

 194

Christopher Bland
Industrial Design & Technology BA

t: +44 (0)7814 778107
e: chris.bland86@btinternet.com

 135

Alex Bolton King
Multimedia Technology & Design BSc

t: +44 (0)7968 956197
e: alex@burningpixels.co.uk
w: www.burningpixels.co.uk

 172

Lottie Booth
Multimedia Technology & Design BSc

t: +44 (0)7751 214389
e: lottie@lottiebooth.com
w: www.lottiebooth.com

172 174

John Andrew Brackett
Product Design BSc

t: +44 (0)7969 498588
e: john_b@hotmail.com
w: www.jbdes.net

 44

Lucy Bradshaw
Industrial Design BSc

t: +44 (0)7940 057202
e: lucyjbradshaw@googlemail.com
w: www.lucyjbradshaw.co.uk

 160   243

Joel Brasher-Jones
Sports Technology BSc

t: +44 (0)7749 139408
e: joel280986@hotmail.com

 46

Dafydd Broom
Mechanical Engineering MEng

e: dafydd.broom@brunelx-team.co.uk

 96

David Brown
Product Design BSc

t: +44 (0)7855 446074
e: db@dajb.co.uk
w: www.dajb.co.uk

 48   49

Dan Buckland
Multimedia Technology & Design BSc

t: +44 (0)7743 426065
e: dan.buckland@btinternet.com
w: www.danbuckland.co.uk

176

Dominic Burton
Industrial Design BSc

t: +44 (0)7881 480519
e: dominicburton@gmail.com
w: www.dominicburton.co.uk

 136   168

Alex Bygrave
Industrial Design BSc

t: +44 (0)7825 047217
e: alex@alexbygrave.co.uk
w: www.alexbygrave.co.uk

 169   244

Anthony James Case
Industrial Design & Technology BA

t: +44 (0)7725 764265

e: ant191@hotmail.co.uk

 50

Madeleine Case
Industrial Design BSc

t: +44 (0)7824 811877

e: mcasedesigns@hotmail.co.uk

w: www.mcasedesigns.co.uk

 108   245

Mabasa Chakawhata
Mechanical Engineering BEng

t: +44 (0)7708 735149

e: mamboseke@googlemail.com

 51

Evangeline Chan
Simon Fraser University

t: +1 778 865 6577

e: evanchan602@gmail.com

 196

Raymond Chan
Simon Fraser University

t: +1 778 896 7099

e: raychan74@shaw.ca

 196

Louise Charouneau
Industrial Design & Technology BA

t: +44 (0)7805 202594

e: louise.charouneau@yahoo.com

w: www.louisecharouneau.com

 52

Jack Cheatle
Industrial Design & Technology BA

t: +44 (0)7944 745891

e: cheatle@hotmail.com

w: www.jackcheatle.com

 54   217

On Ying Cheng
Simon Fraser University

t: +1 778 883 0375

e: chengonying@gmail.com

204

Gavin Chetty
Industrial Design BSc

t: +44 (0)7595 217722

e: gavinchetty@gmail.com

w: www.gavinchetty.com

 56   57

Jency Chong
Multimedia Technology & Design BSc

t: +44 (0)7769 835838

e: jency.chong@googlemail.com

w: www.jencychong.co.uk

 178

Daniel Coveney
Industrial Design & Technology BA

t: +44 (0)7929 763904

e: coveneydan@hotmail.com

 109   137

Matthew Cristofoli
Industrial Design & Technology BA

t: +44 (0)7736 835559

e: mattcristo@yahoo.com

w:

 58

Ryan Lloyd Dee
Industrial Design & Technology BA

t: +44 (0)7876 500430

e: ryanlloyddee@hotmail.com

 60

Rich Drury
Motorsport Engineering MEng

e: rich.drury@brunelracing.co.uk

92

Renhua Du
Tsinghua University
Academy of Arts & Design

 278

Chris Dunne
Multimedia Technology & Design BSc

t: +44 (0)7817 532987

e: chrispdunne@gmail.com

 179

Jin Fan
Simon Fraser University

t: +1 778 288 2077

e: jfan.info@gmail.com

 194   202

Dom Fisher
Multimedia Technology & Design BSc

t: +44 (0)7742 449624

e: dom.fisher@hotmail.com

 180

Kyle Fox
Simon Fraser University

t: +1 907 746 2047

e: exploringfox@mac.com

 198

Jamie Foxen
Industrial Design BSc

t: +44 (0)7977 501248

e: jamiefoxen@hotmail.co.uk

w: www.jamiefoxen.com

 116   138

Rob Fuller
Industrial Design BSc

t: +44 (0)1403 823414
e: fuller.rob@hotmail.com
w: www.rob-fuller.com

▦ 25   ▦ 62

Tom Gentry
Broadcast Media Design & Tech. BSc

t: +44 (0)7834 178071
e: tom.gentry@hotmail.co.uk

◨ 181

Iraklis Georgiadis
Design Strategy & Innovation MA

t: +44 (0)7775 606247
e: iraklis.georgiadis@gmail.com

ⁱⁱ 275

Alan Glazzard
Industrial Design & Technology BA

t: +44 (0)7590 590772
e: aglazzard@yahoo.co.uk

ⁱⁱ 218   ⁱⁱ 246

Ian Goodhead
Product Design BSc

t: +44 (0)7745 641711
e: ian@iangoodhead.com
w: www.iangoodhead.com

▦ 63   ⁱⁱ 247

Oli Gould
Industrial Design BSc

t: +44 (0)7872 071804
e: contactme@oligould.com
w: www.oligould.com

▦ 64   ⁱⁱ 210

Daniel Gray
Broadcast Media Design & Tech. BSc

t: +44 (0)7833 491952
e: dannygray2002@hotmail.com
w: www.dangray.co.uk

◔ 139

Antoine Gripay
Design Strategy & Innovation MA

e: Email: antoniodou7@hotmail.fr

ⁱⁱ 276

Jiawei Gu
Tsinghua University
Academy of Arts & Design

t: +86 1512 000 1765
e: jeffreygu2004@hotmail.com

ⁱⁱ 280

Aakrati Gupta
Product Design BSc

t: +44 (0)7828 485232
e: g.aakrati@gmail.com

◔ 140

Julien Hadley
Industrial Design BSc

t: +44 (0)1728 724167
e: julien_hadley@hotmail.co.uk

 110 248

Mark Haite
Industrial Design & Technology BA

t: +44 (0)7921 174880
e: markhaite@yahoo.co.uk
w: www.haitedesign.co.uk

 65  161

Koogin Han
Design Strategy & Innovation MA

e: email: hkin123@hotmail.com

 276

Sophie Hibbert
Industrial Design BSc

t: +44 (0)7590 569620
e: sophie@sophiehibbertdesign.co.uk
w: www.sophiehibbertdesign.co.uk

 30  249

Kenneth Ho
Simon Fraser University

t: +1 604 715 5751
e: kennethh123@hotmail.com

 196 204

Sandy Holford
Product Design Engineering BSc

t: +44 (0)7799 488867
e: sandy@sandyholford.com
w: www.sandyholford.com

 66 67

Tim Holley
Industrial Design BSc

t: +49 (0) 89 61339630
e: tim@timholley.de
w: www.timholley.de

142  170

Justin Holmes
Simon Fraser University

t: +1 604 569 6068
e: justindanielholmes@gmail.com

198

Tim Holtom
Industrial Design & Technology BA

t: +44 (0)7733 333536
e: timholtom@gmail.com
w: www.timholtom.com

 26 143

Zhang Hui
Tsinghua University
Academy of Arts & Design

 279

Yasmin Idris
Industrial Design BSc

t: +44 (0)7534 964938

e: yasmin_idris@hotmail.com

 117

Sanaz Imanzadeh
Multimedia Technology & Design BSc

t: +44 (0)7737 775497

e: snz_imanzadeh@yahoo.co.uk

 182

Jaclyn A. Immordino
Design & Branding Strategy MA

t: +44 (0)7842 397292

e: jaclyn.immordino@gmail.com

 270

Jung-Yeon Jang
Design & Branding Strategy MA

e: email: ojanejang@googlemail.com

270... 273

Nick John
Motorsport Engineering MEng

e: nick.john@brunelracing.co.uk

92

Kyle Jung
Simon Fraser University

t: +1 778 773 5975

e: kylejung@telus.net

 202

Lucy Kay
Industrial Design BSc

t: +44 (0)7725 535867

e: lucy@ormistoncreative.com

111   144

Renato Kern
Design & Branding Strategy MA

t: +44 (0)7707 672236

e: research@renatokern.com

 271

Marianne Kernohan
Industrial Design BSc

t: +44 (0)7762 364411

e: kernohan@hotmail.co.uk

w: research.renatokern.com

 222   250

Sahir Khan
Mechanical Engineering BEng

t: +44 (0)7877 765700

e: sahir86@gmail.com

 68

David Chi Hang Ko
Simon Fraser University

t: +1 778 883 0090

e: dchk1987@gmail.com

 202

Pui-Jun Lam
Industrial Design BSc

t: +44 (0)7798 621198

e: pui.jun.lam@googlemail.com

 223   251

Frankie Lathbury
Product Design BSc

t: +44 (0)7776 168476

e: frankie.lathbury@live.com

 69

Clare Lee
Multimedia Technology & Design BSc

t: +44 (0)7905 962682

e: clare@clarelee.com

w: www.clarelee.com

 184

Daniel Lee
Simon Fraser University

t: +1 778 858 7207

e: apa_spectre@hotmail.com

198

Jian Li
Tsinghua University
Academy of Arts & Design

281

Andrew Liddle
Industrial Design BSc

t: +44 (0)7849 696806

e: andy_liddle@hotmail.com

 211   252

Henry Lin
Simon Fraser University

t: +1 778 893 3033

e: hwlin85@gmail.com

204

Matthew Littlefield
Mechanical Engineering MEng

t: +44 (0)7704 275710

e: littlefield11@hotmail.com

 99

Qing Liu
Tsinghua University
Academy of Arts & Design

282

My-Binh Ly
Industrial Design BSc

e: m.ly@hotmail.co.uk

⊞ 31   ⊞ 70

Jane Mackay
Motorsport Engineering MEng

e: jane.mackay@brunelracing.co.uk

⊞ 92

Stephen Maclane
Mechanical Engineering MEng

t: +44 (0)7866 636390

e: flat4flamer@hotmail.co.uk

⊞ 99

Justin Mah
Simon Fraser University

e: justin.r.mah@gmail.com

◧ 194   ◧ 202

Michael Malyuk
Simon Fraser University

e: mike.malyuk@gmail.com

◧ 198

Saghar Masihi
Multimedia Technology & Design BSc

t: +44 (0)7963 711906

e: smassihi@yahoo.com

◧ 186

Alex McCarthy
Industrial Design & Technology BA

t: +44 (0)7828 934329

e: alex_mccarthy@fsmail.net

⊞ 71

Jamie McCombe
Mechanical Engineering MEng

e: Jamie.McCombe@brunelx-team.co.uk

⊞ 96

Rebecca McGann
Industrial Design BSc

t: +44 (0)7795 034397

e: beckymcgann@hotmail.co.uk

◌ 112   ⋔ 253

Sam Mclintock
Product Design Engineering BSc

t: +44 (0)7738 538996

e: sammclintock@googlemail.com

w: www.sammclintock.co.uk

⊞ 72   ⊞ 73

Eilís McNulty
Design Strategy & Innovation MA

t: +44 (0)7538 227705

e: eilismcnulty@gmail.com

 275

Rafael Mello
Design & Branding Strategy MA

e: rfgmello@hotmail.com

275

 273

Robert Merriman
Industrial Design & Technology BA

t: +44 (0)7816 489595

e: robmerriman@tiscali.co.uk

 145 231

Gary Mitchell
Product Design BSc

t: +44 (0)7799 104496

e: garymitchelldesign@inbox.com

w: www.garymitchelldesign.com

 74 254

Victoria Monks
Industrial Design BSc

t: +44 (0)7824 828861

e: mail.biz@victoria-monks.com

w: www.victoria-monks.com

 32 75

Mark Montgomerie
Industrial Design & Technology BA

t: +44 (0)7917 732340

e: markmontgomerie@hotmail.com

w: www.markmontgomerie.net

 76

Damon Murray-Morrish
Industrial Design & Technology BA

t: +44 (0)7957 764945

e: damonmmo4@yahoo.co.uk

w: www.murray-morrish.co.uk

 77 162

Shaun Nigel Myles
Design & Branding Strategy MA

t: +44 (0)7881 578859

e: shaun_myles@hotmail.com

w: www.insight4innovation.co.uk

 272

Jea Hoo Na
Design Strategy & Innovation MA

t: +44 (0)7787 157740

e: jna@jeahoo.com

w: www.jeahoo.com

 274

Bill Ng
Simon Fraser University

t: +1 778 558 7950

e: billng53@hotmail.com

 196

Matthew Nourse
Product Design Engineering BSc

t: +44 (0)7790 794305
e: matt@noursedesign.com
w: www.noursedesign.com

▦ 78

Patrick O'Donoghue
Product Design BSc

t: +44 (0)7950 773068
e: info@pod-design.co.uk
w: www.pod-design.co.uk

▦ 80   ♟ 255

Paul O'Hara
Multimedia Technology & Design BSc

t: +44 (0)7952 254443
e: barkallnight@googlemail.com
w: www.paulohara.co.uk

◈ 187

Ainur Orazbayeva
Industrial Design BSc

t: +44 (0)7538 508941
e: ainur.ka@hotmail.com

▦ 36   ◌ 146

James Owen
Mechanical Engineering MEng

e: james.owen@brunelx-team.co.uk

▦ 96

Sarah Parkin
Mechanical Engineering MEng

t: +44 (0)7743 499666
e: sparkin86@hotmail.com

▦ 99

Nital Patel
Industrial Design BSc

t: +44 (0)7595 368103
e: nital.patel@me.com
w: www.nitaldesign.com

▦ 81   ♟ 224

Viral Patel
Multimedia Technology & Design BSc

t: +44 (0)7742 464790
e: motion@viraldoesthis.com
w: www.viraldoesthis.com

◌ 147

Thomas Pegg
Mechanical Engineering MEng

e: tom.pegg@brunelx-team.co.uk

▦ 96

Frederic Perry Phillips
Industrial Design & Technology BA

t: +44 (0)7793 653746
e: fred.86@mac.com

▦ 82   ▦ 83

Pedro Pineda
Industrial Design & Technology BA

e: pedro_pb@live.com
w: www.wecreativepeople.com

⊞ 84   ◌ 123

Ed Powys
Industrial Design & Technology BA

t: +44 (0)7966 065625
e: edpowys@mac.com

⊞ 85

Annika Pugh
Industrial Design & Technology BA

t: +44 (0)7817 655383
e: annikapugh@hotmail.co.uk

◌ 148   ⅱ 225

Kirsten M A Revell
Industrial Design BSc

t: +44 (0)7894 659774
e: kirstenrevell@yahoo.co.uk

ⅱ 226   ⅱ 256

Esteban Schunemann
Industrial Design & Technology BA

t: +44 (0)7947 144149
e: esteban@schunemann.org

⊞ 37   ⊞ 86

Benjamin Scott
Industrial Design BSc

t: +44 (0)7876 298848
e: benjescott@yahoo.com.sg

ⅱ 212   ⅱ 257

Gareth Scott
Industrial Design & Technology BA

t: +44 (0)7590 680918
e: scott.gdesign@gmail.com

ⅱ 258

Kunal Sethi
Industrial Design BSc

t: +44 (0)7939 015573
e: info@kunalsethi.com
w: www.kunalsethi.com

◌ 124   ⅱ 259

Aleksandra Skibicki
Simon Fraser University

t: +1 604 436 4448
e: alex.skibicki@gmail.com

▣ 200

Eden Smith
Virtual Product Design BSc

t: +44 (0)7795 295282
e: eden_cubed@yahoo.com
w: www.geocities.com/eden_cubed

⊞ 87

Harley Smith
Industrial Design & Technology BA

t: +44 (0)7752 268503

e: hhsmith@hotmail.co.uk

 232

Xiaowen Sun
Tsinghua University
Academy of Arts & Design

 283

Sabrina Tan
San Francisco State University

t: +44 (0)779 413443

e: sabrinawtan@gmail.com

 33

Jenny Thai
Simon Fraser University

t: +1 604 816 3882

e: hi.jennythai@gmail.com

 200

Shannon Tinkley
Simon Fraser University

t: +1 778 240 8007

e: shannon.tinkley@gmail.com

w: www.shannontinkley.com

 194

Andy Tomlin
Motorsport Engineering MEng

e: andy.tomlin@brunelracing.co.uk

 92

Dave Townson
Motorsport Engineering MEng

e: dave.townson@brunelracing.co.uk

 92

Siena Tsang
Simon Fraser University

t: +1 604 781 2313

e: sienatsang@hotmail.com

 196

Emil Tschepp
Mechanical Engineering MEng

t: +44 (0)7918 111986

e: e2tschepp@hotmail.com

 99

Ivan Tuen
Design & Branding Strategy MA

t: +44 (0)7846 578121

e: ivantuen@gmail.com

 271

Sarah Turner
Product Design Engineering BSc

t: +44 (0)7917 341452

e: sarah.turner115@googlemail.com

 188

Chloe Underhill
Industrial Design BSc

t: +44 (0)7913 371294

e: underhill_design@live.co.uk

 88   163

James Vardy
Industrial Design BSc

t: +44 (0)7816 981651

e: contact.vardy@gmail.com

 27   260

Juan Francisco Veramendi
San Francisco State University

t: +1 415 320 0337

e: jufra1084@gmail.com

 38

Robert Walsh
Industrial Design & Technology BA

t: +44 (0)7985 431238

e: robert.walsh.1@googlemail.com

 149   233

Alex Weldon
Industrial Design BSc

t: +44 (0)7595 921670

e: alexweldonuk@gmail.com

w: www.alexweldon.co.uk

 150    164

Rhys Welsh
Industrial Design & Technology BA

t: +44 (0)7929 433318

e: info@rhyswelsh.com

w: www.rhyswelsh.com

 89

Anna West
Industrial Design BSc

t: +44 (0)7890 458555

e: annabwest@gmail.com

 118   261

Neil Willetts
Industrial Design BSc

t: +44 (0)7847 668743

e: n.e.n.willetts@gmail.com

 171   262

Karon Wong
Simon Fraser University

t: +1 604 783 2192

e: sienatsang@hotmail.com

 196

Courtney Wood
Industrial Design & Technology BA

t: +44 (0)7791 429282

e: courtney_wood@hotmail.co.uk

 219   263

David Michael Wood
Industrial Design & Technology BA

t: +44 (0)7534 264507

e: david@envizio.co.uk

w: www.envizio.co.uk

 90

Daniel Worboys
Industrial Design BSc

t: +44 (0)7861 249032

e: worboys_3@hotmail.com

w: www.danworboys.com

213   264

Denesa Yip
Simon Fraser University

t: +1 604 780 2687

e: denesayip@gmail.com

 204

Surapen Yosravikul
Design & Branding Strategy MA

t: 44 (0)7516 725494

e: e_willid@hotmail.com

274

Jessica Wai Yee Yu
Simon Fraser University

t: +1 604 838 2684

e: 87.jessicayu@gmail.com

202

Chen Yue
Design & Branding Strategy MA

t: +44 (0)7548 890291

e: yuechen504@hotmail.com

 272

Notes

Notes

thinking out loud

MADE IN BRUNEL™